# Bookkeeping 1

## Workbook

**David Cox**
**Michael Fardon**

## AAT WISE GUIDES – for convenient exam revision

This handy pocket-sized guide provides the **perfect study and revision resource** for the AAT Level 2 Certificate in Accounting.

available for:
Bookkeeping 1
Bookkeeping 2
Working in Accounting and Finance
Introduction to Costing

Visit www.osbornebooks.co.uk for further information and to place your order.

Published by Osborne Books Limited
Unit 1B Everoak Estate
Bromyard Road, Worcester WR2 5HP
Tel 01905 748071
Email books@osbornebooks.co.uk
Website www.osbornebooks.co.uk

Design by Laura Ingham

Printed by CPI Group (UK) Limited, Croydon, CR0 4YY, on environmentally friendly, acid-free paper from managed forests.

MIX
Paper from responsible sources
FSC® C013604
FSC
www.fsc.org

British Library Cataloguing in Publication Data
A catalogue record for this book is available from the British Library

ISBN 978 1909173 026

# Contents

Introduction

## Chapter activities

## Chapter activities – answers

## Practice assessments – tasks

## Practice assessments – answers

# Acknowledgements

The publisher wishes to thank the following for their help with the reading and production of the book: Maz Loton and Cathy Turner. Thanks are also due to Debbie Board for contributing a significant amount of new assessment material, to Hania Lee for her technical reading and to Laura Ingham for her designs for this series.

The publisher is indebted to the Association of Accounting Technicians for its help and advice to our authors and editors during the preparation of this text.

# Authors

**David Cox** has more than twenty years' experience teaching accountancy students over a wide range of levels. Formerly with the Management and Professional Studies Department at Worcester College of Technology, he now lectures on a freelance basis and carries out educational consultancy work in accountancy studies. He is author and joint author of a number of textbooks in the areas of accounting, finance and banking.

**Michael Fardon** has extensive teaching experience of a wide range of banking, business and accountancy courses at Worcester College of Technology. He now specialises in writing business and financial texts and is General Editor at Osborne Books. He is also an educational consultant and has worked extensively in the areas of vocational business curriculum development.

# Introduction

## what this book covers

This book has been written to cover the Unit 'Processing bookkeeping transactions' which is mandatory for the revised (2013) AAT Level 2 Certificate in Accounting.

## what this book contains

This book is set out in two sections:

- **Chapter Activities** which provide extra practice material in addition to the activities included in the Osborne Books Tutorial text. Answers to the Chapter activities are included in this book.

- **Practice Assessments** are provided to prepare the student for the Computer Based Assessments. They are based directly on the structure, style and content of the sample assessment material provided by the AAT at www.aat.org.uk. Suggested answers to the Practice Assessments are set out in this book.

## further information

If you want to know more about our products and resources, please visit www.osbornebooks.co.uk for further details and access to our online shop.

# Chapter activities

# 1   The accounting system

**1.1**   A sale for immediate settlement made at a shop using a bank debit card is known as a:

| | ✔ |
|---|---|
| Cash sale | |
| Credit sale | |
| Debit sale | |

Tick the appropriate box.

**1.2**   An entry in a book of prime entry is:

| | ✔ |
|---|---|
| An entry in the ledger accounts of a business | |
| An entry in the trial balance of a business | |
| The first place an entry is recorded in the accounting records | |

Tick the appropriate box.

**1.3**   The 'ledger' system of accounts is normally set up for recording:

| | ✔ |
|---|---|
| Cash transactions only | |
| Cash and credit transactions only | |
| Cash and credit and other financial transactions | |

Tick the appropriate box.

**1.4**   A sales ledger control account contains the totals of accounts of:

|  | ✔ |
|---|---|
| Customers who buy goods and services on a cash basis | |
| Customers who buy goods and services on a credit basis | |
| Suppliers who provide goods and services on a cash basis | |
| Suppliers who provide goods and services on a credit basis | |

Tick the appropriate box.

**1.5**   Select the missing words from the selection below to complete the following text:

A ................................... *sets out in two columns the balances of the*

................................... *of a business.*

*The* ................................... *of the two columns should* ................................... *The debit column*

*includes the accounts of* ................................... *and the credit column includes the accounts of*

................................... *This provides the* ................................... *of a business with important and*

*useful financial information.*

Choose from:

       **payables**        **agree**        **ledger accounts**        **managers**

       **receivables**        **totals**        **trial balance**

# 2 Financial documents for sales

**2.1** Praxis Stationery has supplied the following goods to a credit customer, Dover Designs.

The list price of the goods is £4.00 per box file, plus VAT at 20%. Dover Designs is to be given a 20% trade discount and a 2% discount for settlement within 14 days.

| DELIVERY NOTE | No 246 |
|---|---|
| **PRAXIS STATIONERY** | **Date** 09 07 20-3 |
| 45 Jarvis Street | |
| Mereford MR1 2GH | |
| | |
| Dover Designs | |
| 68 Whitecliff Street, Granstow, GR3 7GH | Customer code DO109 |

100 Box files, Code BX100

**(a)** **You are to** complete the following invoice:

**INVOICE**  No 1689
**PRAXIS STATIONERY**  **Date** 09 07 20-3
45 Jarvis Street
Mereford MR1 2GH
VAT Reg 831 8627 06

To
Dover Designs
68 Whitecliff Street, Granstow, GR3 7GH

Customer code

Delivery note no

| Quantity | Product code | Unit price (£) | Total (£) | Net (£) | VAT (£) | Total (£) |
|---|---|---|---|---|---|---|
| | | | | | | |
| | | | | | | |
| | | | | | | |

**(b)** If Dover Designs does not settle the invoice within 14 days, Dover designs will have to pay Praxis Stationery a total of:

✔

| | |
|---|---|
| £382.72 | |
| £376.32 | |
| £384.00 | |

Tick the appropriate box.

**2.2** The following transactions have been passed through the account of a Rosetti Associates, a new credit customer of Praxis Limited:

| Date | Document | Amount £ |
|---|---|---|
| 1 August | Invoice 1748 | 4,567.89 |
| 9 August | Invoice 1778 | 2,457.60 |
| 10 August | Invoice 1783 | 4,678.30 |
| 17 August | Credit note 319 | 280.50 |
| 29 August | Cheque | 4,287.39 |

**You are to** complete the statement of account shown below:

**STATEMENT OF ACCOUNT**
**PRAXIS STATIONERY**
45 Jarvis Street, Mereford MR1 2GH

**To** Rosetti Associates
**Date** 31 08 20-3

| Date | Details | Amount £ | Balance outstanding £ |
|---|---|---|---|
| 1 August | Invoice 1748 | | |
| 9 August | Invoice 1778 | | |
| 10 August | Invoice 1783 | | |
| 17 August | Credit note 319 | | |
| 29 August | Cheque | | |

**2.3** Praxis Limited codes all sales invoices with a customer code and a general ledger code.

A selection of the codes used is given below.

| Customer | Customer Account Code |
| --- | --- |
| Artex Ltd | ART09 |
| Bristol Wholesale | BRI25 |
| Britmore Ltd | BRI45 |
| Coleman Trading | COL10 |
| Coldring Limited | COL12 |

| Item | General Ledger Code |
| --- | --- |
| Paper products | GL4002 |
| Pens | GL4003 |
| Storage | GL4008 |
| Printer inks | GL4017 |
| Files | GL4018 |

Indicate in the table below the appropriate customer and general ledger codes that would be applied to the the following sales invoices:

| Product | Customer | General Ledger Code | Customer Code |
| --- | --- | --- | --- |
| Copy paper | Britmore Ltd | | |
| Gel pens | Coldring Limited | | |
| Box files | Artex Limited | | |
| Black printer ink | Coleman Trading | | |
| Archive storage boxes | Bristol Wholesale | | |
| Suspension files | Britmore Limited | | |

**2.4** The financial document which is sent by the seller of goods or services and reduces the amount due to the seller is:

| | ✔ |
|---|---|
| A refund note | |
| A debit note | |
| A credit note | |

Tick the appropriate box.

**2.5** A business sells goods which have a list price of £800. The following discounts are available to the buyer:

- 20% trade discount
- 5% settlement (cash) discount for settlement within 14 days

**(a)** The sales invoice should show a VAT amount (at 20%) of:

| | ✔ |
|---|---|
| £121.60 | |
| £128.00 | |
| £160.00 | |

Tick the appropriate box.

**(b)** The total price for the goods on the invoice should be:

| | ✔ |
|---|---|
| £729.60 | |
| £761.60 | |
| £960.00 | |

Tick the appropriate box.

# 3 Double-entry and the accounting equation

**3.1** Where does double-entry take place?

Select **ONE** option.

| | ✔ |
|---|---|
| In the trial balance | |
| In the books of prime entry | |
| In the ledgers | |
| In the day books | |

**3.2** The ledger which contains the accounts of suppliers who buy on credit is the:

| | ✔ |
|---|---|
| Purchases ledger | |
| General ledger | |
| Sales ledger | |

Which **ONE** of these options is correct?

**3.3** The table below lists payments and receipts of a business which pass through the Bank Account. Write the names of the two accounts involved in the double-entry in the correct columns. The first entry is completed to show what is required. The name of the account which is not the Bank account is shown in bold type in the left-hand column.

|  | Debit | Credit |
|---|---|---|
| Money paid for **Purchases** | Purchases | Bank |
| Money received from **Sales** |  |  |
| **Rent paid** for premises used |  |  |
| **Rent received** for premises let |  |  |
| **Motor expenses** paid |  |  |
| Payment for **advertising** costs |  |  |
| **Stationery** bill paid |  |  |
| **Loan** received |  |  |
| **Loan** repayment made |  |  |

**3.4** The Bank Account shown below has been written up by the bookkeeper, but the double-entry has not yet been done. Use the blank accounts set out on the next page by completing the account name, date details and amount for each entry.

| Dr | | | **Bank Account** | | Cr |
|---|---|---|---|---|---|
| 2013 | | £ | 2013 | | £ |
| 1 Feb | Sales | 5,000 | 1 Feb | Purchases | 3,500 |
| 2 Feb | Sales | 7,500 | 2 Feb | Wages | 2,510 |
| 3 Feb | Bank Loan | 12,500 | 3 Feb | Purchases | 5,000 |
| 5 Feb | Sales | 9,300 | 4 Feb | Rent paid | 780 |

| Debit | | | ....................................Account | | Credit |
|---|---|---|---|---|---|
| Date | Details | £ | Date | Details | £ |
| | | | | | |

| Debit | | | ....................................Account | | Credit |
|---|---|---|---|---|---|
| Date | Details | £ | Date | Details | £ |
| | | | | | |

| Debit | | | ....................................Account | | Credit |
|---|---|---|---|---|---|
| Date | Details | £ | Date | Details | £ |
| | | | | | |

| Debit | | | ....................................Account | | Credit |
|---|---|---|---|---|---|
| Date | Details | £ | Date | Details | £ |
| | | | | | |

| Debit | | | ....................................Account | | Credit |
|---|---|---|---|---|---|
| Date | Details | £ | Date | Details | £ |
| | | | | | |

**3.5**    Financial accounting is based upon the accounting equation.

**(a)**    Show whether the following statements are true or false.

| Statement | True ✔ | False ✔ |
|---|---|---|
| Liabilities equals capital plus assets | | |
| Assets equals liabilities minus capital | | |
| Capital equals assets minus liabilities | | |

**(b)**    Classify each of the following items as an asset or a liability.

| Item | Asset ✔ | Liability ✔ |
|---|---|---|
| Vehicles | | |
| Bank loan | | |
| Money owing by trade receivables | | |
| Inventory | | |
| Cash | | |
| VAT owing to HM Revenue & Customs | | |

**3.6**    Fill in the missing figures:

| Assets £ | Liabilities £ | Capital £ |
|---|---|---|
| 50,000 | 0 | .......... |
| 40,000 | 10,000 | .......... |
| 55,200 | ......... | 30,250 |
| .......... | 18,220 | 40,760 |
| 40,320 | 15,980 | ......... |
| .......... | 24,760 | 48,590 |

**3.7** An increase or a decrease in an asset or liability or capital will result in either a debit or a credit to the asset, liability or capital accounts.

Indicate with a tick whether a debit or credit will result from the transactions in the column on the left.

| Transaction | Debit ✔ | Credit ✔ |
|---|---|---|
| Capital account increases | | |
| Liability account increases | | |
| Asset account decreases | | |
| Liability account decreases | | |
| Asset account increases | | |

**3.8** The table below sets out account balances from the books of a business. The opening capital is £20,000 which has been paid into the business bank account.

The columns (a) to (f) show the account balances resulting from a series of financial transactions that have taken place over time.

**You are to** compare each set of adjacent columns, ie (a) with (b), (b) with (c), and so on and state, with figures, what financial transactions have taken place in each case. The first has been completed for you.

Ignore VAT.

| | (a) | (b) | (c) | (d) | (e) | (f) |
|---|---|---|---|---|---|---|
| | £ | £ | £ | £ | £ | £ |
| **Assets** | | | | | | |
| Vehicles | – | 10,000 | 10,000 | 10,000 | 18,000 | 18,000 |
| Inventory | – | – | 6,000 | 9,000 | 9,000 | 9,000 |
| Bank | 20,000 | 10,000 | 4,000 | 4,000 | 1,000 | 11,000 |
| **Liabilities** | | | | | | |
| Loan | – | – | – | – | 5,000 | 5,000 |
| Payables | – | – | – | 3,000 | 3,000 | 3,000 |
| **Capital** | 20,000 | 20,000 | 20,000 | 20,000 | 20,000 | 30,000 |

*Answer (a) - (b):* Vehicles have been bought for £10,000, paid from the bank

**3.9**  Enter the transactions listed below in the double-entry accounts.  All the transactions pass through the Bank account so you will have to write the entries in the Bank account and work out what the other account entry will be.  No credit sales or purchases are involved.

You can draw up your own accounts, photocopy the accounts on page 69 of the Tutorial, or download blank accounts from the Osborne Books website (www.osbornebooks.co.uk).

| Date 20-4 | Transaction |
| --- | --- |
| 4 March | Paid in capital of £5,000 |
| 5 March | Received bank loan of £15,000 |
| 7 March | Sales of £670 |
| 11 March | Purchases of £375 |
| 15 March | Paid rent of £400 |
| 16 March | Purchases of £1,380 |
| 18 March | Sales of £430 |
| 22 March | Paid telephone bill £180 |
| 26 March | Sales of £1,320 |
| 29 March | Paid insurance of £1,200 |

**3.10** The date is 31 August 20-4. You work as a bookkeeper for Beechwood Tools, a business that sells tools and equipment to the construction trade. You have been asked to balance the four accounts shown below.

**(a)**

| Dr | | | | Egret Building (Sales Ledger) | | Cr |
|---|---|---|---|---|---|---|
| **20-4** | **Details** | **£** | **20-4** | **Details** | **£** | |
| 24 Aug | Sales | 900.00 | 25 Aug | Sales returns | 160.00 | |
| 27 Aug | Sales | 140.00 | | | | |
| 28 Aug | Sales | 360.00 | | | | |

**(b)**

| Dr | | | | Curtis & Curtis (Purchases Ledger) | | Cr |
|---|---|---|---|---|---|---|
| **20-4** | **Details** | **£** | **20-4** | **Details** | **£** | |
| | | | 24 Aug | Purchases | 496.00 | |
| | | | 26 Aug | Purchases | 157.50 | |
| | | | 31 Aug | Purchases | 360.00 | |

**(c)**

| Dr | | | R & T Engineering (Purchases Ledger) | | Cr |
|---|---|---|---|---|---|
| 20-4 | Details | £ | 20-4 | Details | £ |
| 24 Aug | Purchases returns | 160.00 | 25 Aug | Purchases | 240.00 |
| | | | 28 Aug | Purchases | 720.00 |
| | | | 31 Aug | Purchases | 340.00 |

**(d)**

| Dr | | | Motor expenses (General Ledger) | | Cr |
|---|---|---|---|---|---|
| 20-4 | Details | £ | 20-4 | Details | £ |
| 5 Aug | Bank | 150.40 | | | |
| 7 Aug | Bank | 382.00 | | | |
| 9 Aug | Bank | 69.30 | | | |
| 16 Aug | Bank | 126.90 | | | |

## 4  Accounting for sales and sales returns

**4.1**  Which **ONE** of the following is a financial document?

| | ✔ |
|---|---|
| Sales day book | |
| Sales invoice | |
| Sales ledger account of P Lane | |
| Sales account | |

**4.2**  Which **ONE** of the following is in the right order?

| | ✔ |
|---|---|
| Sales returns account; sales ledger control account; customer's account; credit note issued; sales returns day book | |
| Sales returns day book; sales ledger control account; customer's account; sales returns account; credit note issued | |
| Sales returns day book; credit note issued; customer's account; sales returns account; sales ledger control account | |
| Credit note issued; sales returns day book; sales returns account; sales ledger control account; customer's account | |

**4.3**  Which **ONE** of the following is entered in the sales returns day book?

| | ✔ |
|---|---|
| Credit note | |
| Purchase order | |
| Statement of account sent to B Roberts, a trade receivable | |
| Sales invoice | |

For Activities 4.4 and 4.5:

- work in pounds and pence, where appropriate

- the rate of Value Added Tax is to be calculated at 20% (when calculating VAT amounts, you should ignore fractions of a penny, ie round down to a whole penny)

- use a coding system incorporating the following:

| | | | |
|---|---|---|---|
| *sales day book* | *– SDB65* | *general ledger account numbers* | |
| *sales returns day book* | *– SRDB22* | *sales ledger control account* | *– GL1200* |
| | | *sales account* | *– GL4100* |
| *sales ledger account numbers* | | *sales returns account* | *– GL4110* |
| *Dines Stores* | *– SL086* | *Value Added Tax account* | *– GL2200* |
| *Meadow Golf Club* | *– SL135* | | |
| *Raven Retailers Ltd* | *– SL170* | | |
| *Teme Sports Ltd* | *– SL178* | | |
| *Wyvern Stores* | *– SL195* | | |

**4.4**   Pensax Products Limited manufactures and sells sports goods. During November 20-4 the following credit transactions took place:

**20-4**

| | |
|---|---|
| 3 Nov | Sold goods to Dines Stores £265 + VAT, invoice no 3592 issued |
| 5 Nov | Sold goods to Raven Retailers Limited £335 + VAT, invoice no 3593 issued |
| 6 Nov | Sold goods to Meadow Golf Club £175 + VAT, invoice no 3594 issued |
| 10 Nov | Sold goods to Wyvern Stores £455 + VAT, invoice no 3595 issued |
| 11 Nov | Sold goods to Dines Stores £290 + VAT, invoice no 3596 issued |
| 13 Nov | Sold goods to Teme Sports Limited £315 + VAT, invoice no 3597 issued |
| 17 Nov | Sold goods to Raven Retailers Limited £1,120 + VAT, invoice no 3598 issued |
| 19 Nov | Sold goods to Teme Sports Limited £825 + VAT, invoice no 3599 issued |
| 21 Nov | Sold goods to Dines Stores £354 + VAT, invoice no 3600 issued |
| 24 Nov | Sold goods to Meadow Golf Club £248 + VAT, invoice no 3601 issued |
| 27 Nov | Sold goods to Wyvern Stores £523 + VAT, invoice no 3602 issued |

**You are to:**

**(a)**   Enter the above transactions in Pensax Products' sales day book for November 20-4, using the format shown on the next page.

**(b)**   Record the accounting entries in Pensax Products' general ledger and sales ledger. (You will need to retain the ledger accounts for use with Activity 4.5.).

| Sales Day Book | | | | | | SDB65 |
|---|---|---|---|---|---|---|
| Date | Details | Invoice number | Account code | Total £ | VAT £ | Net £ |
| | | | | | | |
| | | | | | | |
| | | | | | | |
| | | | | | | |
| | | | | | | |
| | | | | | | |

**4.5**   The following details are the sales returns of Pensax Products Limited for November 20-4. They are to be:

**(a)**   Entered in the sales returns day book for November 20-4, using the format shown on the next page.

**(b)**   Recorded in the general ledger and sales ledger (use the ledgers already prepared in the answer to Activity 4.4).

**20-4**

| | |
|---|---|
| 10 Nov | Dines Stores returns goods £55 + VAT, credit note no 831 issued |
| 14 Nov | Wyvern Stores returns goods £60 + VAT, credit note no 832 issued |
| 19 Nov | Meadow Golf Club returns goods £46 + VAT, credit note no 833 issued |
| 24 Nov | Teme Sports Limited returns goods £127 + VAT, credit note no 834 issued |
| 28 Nov | Dines Stores returns goods £87 + VAT, credit note no 835 issued |

| Sales Returns Day Book | | | | | | SRDB22 |
|---|---|---|---|---|---|---|
| Date | Details | Credit note number | Account code | Total £ | VAT £ | Net £ |
|  |  |  |  |  |  |  |
|  |  |  |  |  |  |  |
|  |  |  |  |  |  |  |

**4.6** Sales invoices have been prepared and partially entered in the sales day book, as shown below.

**(a)** Complete the entries in the sales day book by inserting the appropriate figures for each invoice.

**(b)** Total the last five columns of the sales day book.

**Sales day book**

| Date 20-4 | Details | Invoice number | Total £ | VAT £ | Net £ | Sales type 1 £ | Sales type 2 £ |
|---|---|---|---|---|---|---|---|
| 30 June | Olander Ltd | 1895 |  | 320 |  | 1,600 |  |
| 30 June | Boltz & Co | 1896 | 5,040 |  |  |  | 4,200 |
| 30 June | Ravells | 1897 | 576 | 480 | 480 |  |  |
|  | Totals |  |  |  |  |  |  |

**4.7** You are employed by Beacon Limited as an accounts assistant. The business has a manual accounting system. Double-entry takes place in the general ledger; individual accounts of trade receivables are kept as subsidiary accounts in the sales ledger. The VAT rate is 20%.

**Notes:**

- show your answer with a tick, words or figures, as appropriate
- coding is not required

**(a)** The following credit transactions all took place on 30 June 20-7 and have been entered into the sales day book as shown below. No entries have yet been made in the ledgers.

**Sales day book**

| Date 20-7 | Details | Invoice number | Total £ | VAT £ | Net £ |
|---|---|---|---|---|---|
| 30 June | Upton Ltd | 407 | 2,016 | 336 | 1,680 |
| 30 June | Bromyards | 408 | 3,408 | 568 | 2,840 |
| 30 June | Kempsey & Co | 409 | 4,272 | 712 | 3,560 |
| 30 June | Fernhill plc | 410 | 2,448 | 408 | 2,040 |
| | Totals | | 12,144 | 2,024 | 10,120 |

What will be the entries in the sales ledger?

Select your account names from the following list: Bromyards, Fernhill plc, Kempsey & Co, Purchases, Purchases ledger control, Purchases returns, Sales, Sales ledger control, Sales returns, Upton Ltd, Value Added Tax.

**Sales ledger**

| Account name | Amount £ | Debit ✓ | Credit ✓ |
|---|---|---|---|
| | | | |
| | | | |
| | | | |
| | | | |

What will be the entries in the general ledger?

Select your account names from the following list: Purchases, Purchases ledger control, Purchases returns, Sales, Sales ledger control, Sales returns, Value Added Tax.

**General ledger**

| Account name | Amount £ | Debit ✔ | Credit ✔ |
|---|---|---|---|
| | | | |
| | | | |
| | | | |

**(b)** The following credit transactions all took place on 30 June 20-7 and have been entered into the sales returns day book as shown below. No entries have yet been made in the ledgers.

**Sales returns day book**

| Date 20-7 | Details | Credit note number | Total £ | VAT £ | Net £ |
|---|---|---|---|---|---|
| 30 June | Drake & Co | CN 84 | 336 | 56 | 280 |
| 30 June | Hanbury Trading | CN 85 | 1,008 | 168 | 840 |
| | Totals | | 1,344 | 224 | 1,120 |

What will be the entries in the sales ledger?

Select your account names from the following list: Drake & Co, Hanbury Trading, Purchases, Purchases ledger control, Purchases returns, Sales, Sales ledger control, Sales returns, Value Added Tax.

**Sales ledger**

| Account name | Amount £ | Debit ✔ | Credit ✔ |
|---|---|---|---|
| | | | |
| | | | |

What will be the entries in the general ledger?

Select your account names from the following list: Purchases, Purchases ledger control, Purchases returns, Sales, Sales ledger control, Sales returns, Value Added Tax.

**General ledger**

| Account name | Amount £ | Debit ✔ | Credit ✔ |
|---|---|---|---|
| | | | |
| | | | |
| | | | |

**4.8**   You are the bookkeeper at Rankin Ltd.

Four sales invoices have been issued and have been partially entered in the analysed sales day book, shown below.

Complete the entries in the sales day book by inserting the appropriate details from each invoice, and then total the day book.

| | |
|---|---|
| **INVOICE NO 2132** | 30 June 20-4 |
| **From: Rankin Ltd** | |
| 18 Blenheim Road | |
| Linton | |
| LT4 5JE | |
| VAT Registration No 264 1432 55 | |

| | | £ |
|---|---|---|
| **To:** | Hawke Ltd | |
| | 30 items of product T12 @ £10 each | 300.00 |
| | VAT @ 20% | 60.00 |
| | Total | 360.00 |

| | |
|---|---|
| **INVOICE NO 2133** | 30 June 20-4 |
| **From: Rankin Ltd** | |
| 18 Blenheim Road | |
| Linton | |
| LT4 5JE | |
| VAT Registration No 264 1432 55 | |

| | | £ |
|---|---|---|
| **To:** | T Martin | |
| | 25 items of product S12 @ £15 each | 375.00 |
| | VAT @ 20% | 75.00 |
| | Total | 450.00 |

**INVOICE NO 2134**                    30 June 20-4

**From: Rankin Ltd**

18 Blenheim Road

Linton

LT4 5JE

VAT Registration No 264 1432 55

| To: | S Garner | £ |
|---|---|---|
| | 35 items of product S12 @ £15 each | 525.00 |
| | VAT @ 20% | 105.00 |
| | Total | 630.00 |

**INVOICE NO 2135**                    30 June 20-4

**From: Rankin Ltd**

18 Blenheim Road

Linton

LT4 5JE

VAT Registration No 264 1432 55

| To: | JEC Ltd | £ |
|---|---|---|
| | 15 items of product T12 @ £10 each | 150.00 |
| | VAT @ 20% | 30.00 |
| | Total | 180.00 |

**Sales day book**

| Date 20-4 | Details | Invoice number | Total £ | VAT £ | Net £ | Product S12 £ | Product T12 £ |
|---|---|---|---|---|---|---|---|
| 30 June | Hawke Ltd | | | | | | |
| 30 June | T Martin | | | | | | |
| 30 June | S Garner | | | | | | |
| 30 June | JEC Ltd | | | | | | |
| | **Totals** | | | | | | |

# 5 | Process payments from customers

**5.1** A business receiving a remittance advice from a customer will need to check it against the sales documents. Which of the following checks is required?

Choose the correct option.

| | ✔ |
|---|---|
| Sales documention reference numbers | |
| The number of the cheque | |
| Bank account number | |
| Date of the remittance advice | |

**5.2** A business receiving a cheque from a customer in payment of an invoice will need to check it to make sure that it is in order. Which of the following list of checks is correct?

Choose the appropriate option.

| | ✔ |
|---|---|
| Date, signature, bank account number | |
| Date, signature, bank sort code | |
| Same amount in words and figures, in date, signature of customer | |
| Same amount in words and figures, in date, invoice number | |

**5.3**

The account shown below is in the sales ledger of Johnston & Co. Also shown below is a BACS remittance advice received from R Romero at the end of August.

| | | | | | |
|---|---|---|---|---|---|
| **R Romero** | | | | | |
| **Date 20-4** | **Details** | **Amount £** | **Date 20-4** | **Details** | **Amount £** |
| 1 Aug | Balance b/f | 2,790 | 2 Aug | Bank | 2,790 |
| 10 Aug | Sales invoice 392 | 690 | 26 June | Sales returns credit note 295 | 90 |
| 25 Aug | Sales Invoice 417 | 1,100 | | | |

| | | |
|---|---|---|
| **R Romero** | | |
| **BACS REMITTANCE ADVICE** | | |
| To: Johnston & Co | | Date: 28 August 20-4 |
| The following payment will reach your bank account within 3 working days. | | |
| **Invoice number** | **Credit note number** | **Amount £** |
| 392 | | 590 |
| 417 | | 1,100 |
| Total amount paid | | 1,690 |

You are required to check the remittance advice against the sales ledger account.

State two discrepancies you can identify:

**(a)**

**(b)**

# 6 Process documents from suppliers

6.1 When a credit note is received by the buyer in respect of faulty goods returned by the buyer, it should be checked against the details on the:

| | ✔ |
|---|---|
| Invoice | |
| Delivery note | |
| Remittance advice | |

Tick the appropriate box.

6.2 A business will use supplier codes to refer to accounts in:

| | ✔ |
|---|---|
| The general ledger | |
| The sales ledger | |
| The purchases ledger | |

Tick the appropriate box.

6.3 A business will use general ledger codes to refer to accounts for:

| | ✔ |
|---|---|
| Purchases | |
| Suppliers | |
| Customers | |

Tick the appropriate box.

**6.4** A supply of office chairs has been delivered to Praxis Stationery. Praxis Stationery completes a Goods Received Note as shown below.

Examine the note and answer the questions below by selecting the correct words from the following list:

| | | | |
|---|---|---|---|
| **Praxis Stationery** | **2 chairs missing** | **2 chairs damaged** | **purchases day book** |
| **credit note** | **Helicon Furniture** | **debit note** | **sales day book** |
| **sales ledger** | **returns note** | **refund note** | **purchase ledeger** |

---

**GOODS RECEIVED NOTE**
**PRAXIS STATIONERY**

GRN no.      302

supplier      Helicon Furniture

date           4 December 20-4

| order ref. | quantity | description |
|---|---|---|
| 8246 | 10 | Office chairs (Code Typ72652) |

received by....*D Nutt*.........................checked by....*N Mason*....

**condition of goods**    condition - *good (8 chairs)*
                          damages - *2 chairs damaged*
                          shortages *none*

---

**(a)** Who has supplied the chairs?

**(b)** What is the problem with the consignment?

**(c)** What document would be issued by the supplier to adjust the account of Praxis Stationery?

**(d)** Where in the supplier's accounting records would the account of Praxis Stationery be maintained?

**6.5** A supply of office chairs has been delivered to Praxis Stationery by Firth Furniture. The purchase order sent from Praxis Stationery, and the invoice from Firth Furniture, are shown below.

---

## PURCHASE ORDER
**PRAXIS STATIONERY**

45 Jarvis Street, Mereford MR1 2GH

**No** 1066
**Date** 10 08 20-3

---

To: Firth Furniture

Please supply 12 Executive office chairs (product code EXCH45)

Purchase price: £150 each, plus VAT @ 20%

Discount: less 20% trade discount, as agreed

---

## INVOICE
### FIRTH FURNITURE
17 Chippendale Street
Lesspool LP1 5HG
VAT Reg 171 7326 11

To:
Praxis Stationery
45 Jarvis Street, Mereford MR1 2GH

Date 11 08 20-3
No. 6518
Account PS6232

| Quantity | Product code | Price (£) | Total (£) | Net (£) | VAT (£) | Total (£) |
|----------|-------------|-----------|-----------|---------|---------|-----------|
| 12 | EXCH45 | 150.00 | 1,800.00 | 1,620.00 | 324.00 | 1,944.00 |

Check the invoice against the purchase order and answer the following questions:

| | |
|---|---|
| Has the correct purchase price of the chairs been charged? Yes or No? | |
| Has the correct discount been applied? Yes or No? | |
| What would be the VAT amount charged if the invoice was correct? | £ |
| What would be the total amount charged if the invoice was correct? | £ |

**6.6** A supply of office desks has been delivered to Praxis Stationery by Firth Furniture. The purchase order sent from Praxis Stationery, and the delivery note from Firth Furniture, are shown below.

---

## PURCHASE ORDER
**PRAXIS STATIONERY**

**No** 1261
**Date** 05 09 20-3

45 Jarvis Street, Mereford MR1 2GH

---

To: Firth Furniture

Please supply  4 oak finish office tables (product code OTT28)

Purchase price: £80 each, plus VAT @ 20%.

Discount: less 20% trade discount, as agreed.

---

## DELIVERY NOTE
### FIRTH FURNITURE
17 Chippendale Street
Lesspool LP1 5HG
VAT Reg 171 7326 11

To:
Praxis Stationery
45 Jarvis Street, Mereford MR1 2GH

Date 10 09 20-3
No. 6610
Account PS6232

| Quantity | Product code | Description |
|---|---|---|
| 5 | OTT28 | Office tables, teak finish (product code OTT28) @ £80 each, less trade discount @ 20%, plus VAT @ 20%. |

Check the delivery note against the purchase order and answer the following questions:

| | |
|---|---|
| Has the correct number of tables been supplied? Yes or No? | |
| Has the correct type of table been supplied? Yes or No? | |
| What will be the total of the invoice on the basis of the details on the delivery note? | £ |
| If a credit note were issued, what would be the total, including VAT? | £ |

# 7 Accounting for purchases and purchases returns

**7.1** Which **ONE** of the following is a financial document?

| | ✔ |
|---|---|
| Purchases invoice | |
| Statement of account sent by T Lewis, a trade payable | |
| Purchases day book | |
| Purchases ledger control account | |

**7.2** Which **ONE** of the following is in the right order?

| | ✔ |
|---|---|
| Purchases day book; purchases ledger control account; invoice received; purchases account; supplier's account | |
| Purchases account; supplier's account; purchases ledger control account; purchases day book; invoice received | |
| Invoice received; purchases day book; purchases account; purchases ledger control account; supplier's account | |
| Invoice received; purchases account; purchases ledger control account; supplier's account; purchases day book | |

**7.3** Which **ONE** of the following shows the correct general ledger entries to record the purchase of goods for resale on credit?

| | ✔ |
|---|---|
| Debit purchases ledger control; debit VAT; credit purchases | |
| Debit purchases ledger control; credit purchases; credit VAT | |
| Debit purchases; debit VAT; credit purchases ledger control | |
| Debit purchases; credit purchases ledger control; credit VAT | |

For Activities 7.4 and 7.5:

- work in pounds and pence, where appropriate

- the rate of Value Added Tax is to be calculated at 20% (when calculating VAT amounts, you should ignore fractions of a penny, ie round down to a whole penny)

- use a coding system incorporating the following:

| | | | |
|---|---|---|---|
| purchases day book | – PDB55 | general ledger account numbers | |
| purchases returns day book | – PRDB14 | purchases ledger control account | – GL2350 |
| | | purchases account | – GL5100 |
| purchases ledger account numbers | | purchases returns account | – GL5110 |
| S Burston | – PL530 | Value Added Tax account | – GL2200 |
| Iley Supplies Ltd | – PL605 | | |
| Malvern Manufacturing | – PL625 | | |
| SG Enterprises | – PL720 | | |

**7.4**  Wyvern Products Limited manufactures and sells garden furniture. During May 20-2 the following credit transactions took place:

**20-2**

3 May   Purchased goods from Malvern Manufacturing £170 + VAT, invoice no 7321

9 May   Purchased goods from S Burston £265 + VAT, invoice no SB745

12 May  Purchased goods from Iley Supplies Ltd £450 + VAT, invoice no 4721

18 May  Purchased goods from SG Enterprises £825 + VAT, invoice no 3947

23 May  Purchased goods from S Burston £427 + VAT, invoice no SB773

30 May  Purchased goods from Malvern Manufacturing £364 + VAT, invoice no 7408

**You are to:**

**(a)**  Enter the above transactions in Wyvern Products Limited's purchases day book for May 20-2, using the format shown on the next page.

**(b)**  Record the accounting entries in Wyvern Products Limited's general ledger and purchases ledger. (You will need to retain the ledger accounts for use with Activity 7.5).

| Date | Details | Invoice number | Account code | Total £ | VAT £ | Net £ |
|------|---------|----------------|--------------|---------|-------|-------|
|      |         |                |              |         |       |       |
|      |         |                |              |         |       |       |

Purchases Day Book — PDB55

**7.5** The following are the purchases returns of Wyvern Products Limited for May 20-2. They are to be:

**(a)** Entered in the purchases returns day book for May 20-2, using the format shown on the next page.

**(b)** Recorded in the general ledger and purchases ledger (use the ledgers already prepared in the answer to Activity 7.4).

**20-2**

11 May   Returned goods to Malvern Manufacturing £70 + VAT, credit note no CN345 received

17 May   Returned goods to Iley Supplies Ltd £85 + VAT, credit note no CN241 received

24 May   Returned goods to SG Enterprises £25 + VAT, credit note no 85 received

31 May   Returned goods to S Burston £55 + VAT, credit note no SB95 received

| Purchases Returns Day Book | | | | Total | VAT | PRDB14 Net |
|---|---|---|---|---|---|---|
| Date | Details | Credit note number | Account code | £ | £ | £ |
| | | | | | | |
| | | | | | | |
| | | | | | | |

**7.6** Purchases invoices have been prepared and partially entered in the purchases day book, as shown below.

(a) Complete the entries in the purchases day book by inserting the appropriate figures for each invoice.

(b) Total the last five columns of the purchases day book.

**Purchases day book**

| Date 20-4 | Details | Invoice number | Total £ | VAT £ | Net £ | Purchases type 1 £ | Purchases type 2 £ |
|---|---|---|---|---|---|---|---|
| 30 June | King & Co | K641 | 2,016 | | 1,680 | | 1,680 |
| 30 June | Rossingtons | 2129 | | 512 | | 2,560 | |
| 30 June | Moniz Ltd | M/149 | 2,208 | | | | 1,840 |
| | Totals | | | | | | |

**7.7** You are employed by Churchtown Limited as an accounts assistant. The business has a manual accounting system. Double-entry takes place in the general ledger; individual accounts of payables are kept as memorandum accounts in the purchases ledger. The VAT rate is 20%.

**Notes:**

- show your answer with a tick, words or figures, as appropriate
- coding is not required

**(a)** The following credit transactions all took place on 30 June 20-8 and have been entered into the purchases day book as shown below. No entries have yet been made in the ledgers.

**Purchases day book**

| Date 20-8 | Details | Invoice number | Total £ | VAT £ | Net £ |
|---|---|---|---|---|---|
| 30 June | H & L Ltd | 5986 | 6,528 | 1,088 | 5,440 |
| 30 June | Sperrin & Co | P864 | 2,208 | 368 | 1,840 |
| 30 June | Hickmores | H591 | 4,608 | 768 | 3,840 |
| 30 June | Marklew plc | 6417 | 1,104 | 184 | 920 |
| | Totals | | 14,448 | 2,408 | 12,040 |

What will be the entries in the purchases ledger?

Select your account names from the following list: H & L Ltd, Hickmores, Marklew plc, Purchases, Purchases ledger control, Purchases returns, Sales, Sales ledger control, Sales returns, Sperrin & Co, Value Added Tax.

**Purchases ledger**

| Account name | Amount £ | Debit ✔ | Credit ✔ |
|---|---|---|---|
| | | | |
| | | | |
| | | | |
| | | | |

What will be the entries in the general ledger?

Select your account names from the following list: Purchases, Purchases ledger control, Purchases returns, Sales, Sales ledger control, Sales returns, Value Added Tax.

**General ledger**

| Account name | Amount £ | Debit ✔ | Credit ✔ |
|---|---|---|---|
|  |  |  |  |
|  |  |  |  |
|  |  |  |  |

**(b)**  The following credit transactions all took place on 30 June 20-8 and have been entered into the purchases returns day book as shown below. No entries have yet been made in the ledgers.

**Purchases returns day book**

| Date 20-8 | Details | Credit note number | Total £ | VAT £ | Net £ |
|---|---|---|---|---|---|
| 30 June | Marcer Transport | 564 | 624 | 104 |  |
| 30 June | Schuller Ltd | CN28 | 432 | 72 | 360 |
|  | Totals |  | 1,056 | 176 | 880 |

What will be the entries in the purchases ledger?

Select your account names from the following list: Marcer Transport, Purchases, Purchases ledger control, Purchases returns, Sales, Sales ledger control, Sales returns, Schuller Ltd, Value Added Tax.

**Purchases ledger**

| Account name | Amount £ | Debit ✔ | Credit ✔ |
|---|---|---|---|
|  |  |  |  |
|  |  |  |  |

What will be the entries in the general ledger?

Select your account names from the following list: Purchases, Purchases ledger control, Purchases returns, Sales, Sales ledger control, Sales returns, Value Added Tax.

**General ledger**

| Account name | Amount £ | Debit ✔ | Credit ✔ |
|---|---|---|---|
|  |  |  |  |
|  |  |  |  |
|  |  |  |  |

**7.8**   You are the bookkeeper at Rankin Ltd.

Four purchases invoices have been received and have been partially entered in the analysed purchases day book, shown below.

Complete the entries in the purchases day book by inserting the appropriate details from each invoice, and then total the day book.

---

**INVOICE NO 4681**                                30 June 20-4

**From:  Lyster Ltd**

    44 Mill Street

    Linton

    LT3 6AJ

    VAT Registration No 451 3268 01

---

**To:**      Rankin Ltd                                          £

          100 items of product S12 @ £10 each       1,000.00

          VAT @ 20%                                   200.00

          Total                                     1,200.00

---

**INVOICE NO 6234**                                30 June 20-4

**From:  T England**

    14 Nelson Street

    Westerham

    WH6 9JK

    VAT Registration No 323 8614 25

---

**To:**      Rankin Ltd                                          £

          60 items of product T12 @ £6 each          360.00

          VAT @ 20%                                    72.00

          Total                                       432.00

INVOICE NO 1634                                    30 June 20-4

From: **Mere Ltd**

22 Moreton Road

Ruddington

RT5 2BN

VAT Registration No 495 0232 55

| | | £ |
|---|---|---|
| **To:** | Rankin Ltd | |
| | 150 items of product T12 @ £6 each | 900.00 |
| | VAT @ 20% | 180.00 |
| | Total | 1,080.00 |

INVOICE NO 8561                                    30 June 20-4

From: **J Mehta**

84 The High Road

Linton

LT1 2DS

VAT Registration No 264 9781 65

| | | £ |
|---|---|---|
| **To:** | Rankin Ltd | |
| | 40 items of product S12 @ £10 each | 400.00 |
| | VAT @ 20% | 80.00 |
| | Total | 480.00 |

**Purchases day book**

| Date 20-4 | Details | Invoice number | Total £ | VAT £ | Net £ | Product S12 £ | Product T12 £ |
|---|---|---|---|---|---|---|---|
| 30 June | Lyster Ltd | | | | | | |
| 30 June | T England | | | | | | |
| 30 June | Mere Ltd | | | | | | |
| 30 June | J Mehta | | | | | | |
| | **Totals** | | | | | | |

# 8 Prepare payments to suppliers

**8.1** If a supplier duplicates an invoice for goods ordered, the likely effect will be:

| | ✔ |
|---|---|
| An increase in the total amount owing shown on the statement of account | |
| A decrease in the total amount owing shown on the statement of account | |
| No effect at all | |

Tick the appropriate box.

**8.2** A remittance advice is likely to show details of the following financial documents issued:

| | ✔ |
|---|---|
| Purchase invoices, purchase credit notes, goods received notes | |
| Purchase invoices, purchase credit notes, cheques issued | |
| Purchase invoices, purchase credit notes, total amount owing | |

Tick the appropriate box.

**8.3** The purchase ledger account of a supplier shows a purchase invoice which is not shown on the supplier's statement of account. This:

| | ✔ |
|---|---|
| Can be adjusted by asking the supplier to issue a credit note | |
| Will reduce the total amount shown as owing on the statement of account | |
| Will increase the total amount shown as owing on the statement of account | |

Tick the appropriate box.

**8.4** Shown below is a statement of account received from Masters Supplies, a credit supplier, and the supplier's account as shown in the purchases ledger of Broadfield Traders.

### Masters Supplies

**21 HighStreet, East Mereford, MR7 9HJ**

To: Broadfield Traders

Unit 18 Elgar Estate

Mereford, MR2 5FG          **STATEMENT OF ACCOUNT**

| Date 20-4 | Invoice Number | Details | Invoice Amount £ | Cheque Amount £ | Balance £ |
|---|---|---|---|---|---|
| 1 May | 699 | Goods | 2,000 | | 2,000 |
| 5 May | 712 | Goods | 1,100 | | 3,100 |
| 9 May | 731 | Goods | 750 | | 3,850 |
| 28 May | 790 | Goods | 1,360 | | 5,210 |
| 1 June | - | Cheque | | 3,850 | 1,360 |

| | | Masters Supplies | | | | |
|---|---|---|---|---|---|---|
| Date 20-4 | Details | | Amount £ | Date 20-4 | Details | Amount £ |
| 1 June | Bank | | 3,850 | 1 May | Purchases | 2,000 |
| 28 June | Bank | | 1,000 | 8 May | Purchases | 1,100 |
| | | | | 10 May | Purchases | 750 |

(a) Which item is missing from the statement of account from Masters Supplies? *Select your answer from the following list:*

Invoice 699, Invoice 712, Invoice 731, Invoice 790, Cheque for £3,850, Cheque for £1,000

(b) Which item is missing from the supplier account in Broadfield Traders' purchases ledger? *Select your answer from the following list:*

Invoice 699, Invoice 712, Invoice 731, Invoice 790, Cheque for £3,850, Cheque for £1,000

(c) Assuming any differences between the statement of account from Masters Supplies and the supplier account in Broadfield Traders' purchases ledger are simply due to omission errors, what is the amount owing to Masters Supplies?

£

**8.5** Mereford Traders sends BACS remittance advice notes to suppliers on the last day of the month following the month of invoice. Mereford Traders banks with National Bank plc and A Strauss & Co banks with Mercia Bank plc. Below is an uncompleted BACS remittance advice and an extract from Mereford Trader's purchases ledger.

# Mereford Traders
45 College Street
Mereford, MR3 4GT

**BACS REMITTANCE ADVICE**

To:                                                                      Date:

The following payment will reach your bank account within 3 working days.

| Invoice number | Credit note number | Amount £ |
|---|---|---|
| | | |
| | Total amount paid | |

| A Strauss & Co | | | | | |
|---|---|---|---|---|---|
| Date 20-4 | Details | Amount £ | Date 20-4 | Details | Amount £ |
| 3 Feb | Purchases returns credit note CN101 | 400 | 15 Feb | Purchases Invoice 2250 | 1,750 |
| 20 Mar | Purchases returns credit note CN105 | 300 | 12 Mar | Purchases Invoice 2461 | 2,340 |
| 30 Mar | Bank | 1,350 | 29 Mar | Purchases Invoice 2479 | 1,600 |
| | | | 10 Apl | Purchases Invoice 2499 | 2,107 |

**(a)** The BACS remittance advice will be sent:

| | ✔ |
|---|---|
| With a cheque to Mereford Traders | |
| Without a cheque to A Strauss & Co | |
| To Mercia Bank plc with a cheque | |
| To Mercia Bank plc without a cheque | |

Select the correct option.

**(b)**    What will be the date shown on the BACS remittance advice?

|  | ✔ |
|---|---|
| 28 February |  |
| 31 March |  |
| 30 April |  |
| 31 May |  |

Select the correct option.

**(c)**    What will be the items shown on the BACS remittance advice?

|  | ✔ |
|---|---|
| Invoice 2250, Invoice 2461, invoice 2479, invoice 2687 |  |
| Invoice 2461, invoice 2479, credit note CN105 |  |
| Invoice 2250, Invoice 2461, invoice 2479, credit note CN101 |  |
| Invoice 2250, Invoice 2461, credit note CN101, credit note CN105 |  |

Select the correct option.

**(d)**    The amount of the remittance advice will be:

|  | ✔ |
|---|---|
| £3,390 |  |
| £4,990 |  |
| £3,640 |  |
| £5,390 |  |

Select the correct option.

# 9  Three column cash book

**9.1**   The discount allowed column of the cash book is totalled at regular intervals and transferred to:

| | ✔ |
|---|---|
| The credit side of discount allowed account | |
| The debit side of discount allowed account | |
| The debit side of sales account | |
| The credit side of sales account | |

**9.2**   The following transactions all took place on 30 June and have been entered in the debit side of the cash book of Jane Martin, as shown below. No entries have yet been made in the ledgers.

Note that Jane Martin's business is not registered for Value Added Tax.

**Cash book – debit side**

| Date 20-4 | Details | Discounts £ | Cash £ | Bank £ |
|---|---|---|---|---|
| 30 June | Balance b/f | | | 2,076 |
| 30 June | Boscawen Ltd | 45 | | 1,540 |

**(a)**   What will be the entries in the sales ledger?

Select your account names from the following list: Balance b/f, Bank, Boscawen Ltd, Discounts allowed, Discounts received, Purchases ledger control, Sales ledger control.

**Sales ledger**

| Account name | Amount £ | Debit ✔ | Credit ✔ |
|---|---|---|---|
| | | | |
| | | | |

**(b)**  What will be the entries in the general ledger?

Select your account names from the following list: Balance b/f, Bank, Boscawen Ltd, Discounts allowed, Discounts received, Purchases ledger control, Sales ledger control.

**General ledger**

| Account name | Amount £ | Debit ✔ | Credit ✔ |
|---|---|---|---|
| | | | |
| | | | |
| | | | |

The following transactions all took place on 30 June and have been entered in the credit side of the cash book of Jane Martin, as shown below. No entries have yet been made in the ledgers.

**Cash book – credit side**

| Date 20-4 | Details | Discounts £ | Cash £ | Bank £ |
|---|---|---|---|---|
| 30 June | Wages | | 1,265 | |
| 30 June | Office equipment | | | 1,968 |

**(c)**  What will be the entries in the general ledger?

Select your account name from the following list: Bank, Office equipment, Purchases ledger control, Sales ledger control, Wages.

**General ledger**

| Account name | Amount £ | Debit ✔ | Credit ✔ |
|---|---|---|---|
| | | | |
| | | | |

**9.3**   The following transactions all took place on 30 June 20-4 and have been entered into the cash book of Rafe Sadler, as shown below. No entries have yet been made in the ledgers.

Note that Rafe Sadler's business is not registered for Value Added Tax.

| Dr | | | | | | Cash Book | | | CB73 | | Cr |
|---|---|---|---|---|---|---|---|---|---|---|---|
| Date | Details | Discounts | Cash | Bank | Date | Details | | Discounts | Cash | Bank | |
| 20-4 | | | £ | £ | 20-4 | | | | £ | £ | |
| 30 Jun | Balances b/f | | 250 | 3,840 | 30 Jun | Wages | | | | 1,175 | |
| 30 Jun | Smithsons Ltd | | | | 30 Jun | Rent | | | | 1,200 | |
| | (trade receivable) | 100 | | 2,750 | 30 Jun | Stationery | | | 120 | | |
| | | | | | 30 Jun | Balances c/d | | | 130 | 4,215 | |
| | | | 250 | 6,590 | | | | | 250 | 6,590 | |
| 1 Jul | Balances b/d | | 130 | 4,215 | | | | | | | |

**(a)**   What will be the entries in the sales ledger?

Select your account names from the following list: Balance b/f, Bank, Discounts allowed, Discounts received, Purchases ledger control, Sales Ledger control, Smithsons Ltd.

**Sales ledger**

| Account name | Amount £ | Debit ✔ | Credit ✔ |
|---|---|---|---|
| | | | |
| | | | |

**(b)**   What will be the entries in the general ledger?

Select your account names from the following list: Balance b/f, Bank, Discounts allowed, Discounts received, Purchases ledger control, Rent, Sales ledger control, Stationery, Smithsons Ltd, Wages.

**General ledger**

| Account name | Amount £ | Debit ✔ | Credit ✔ |
|---|---|---|---|
| | | | |
| | | | |
| | | | |
| | | | |
| | | | |
| | | | |

**9.4** The following cash book shows a number of transactions of Wentworths which all took place on 30 September 20-1:

| Dr | | | | | **Cash Book** | | | | **CB68** | | **Cr** |
|---|---|---|---|---|---|---|---|---|---|---|---|
| Date | Details | Acc code | Discounts | Cash | Bank | Date | Details | Acc code | Discounts | Cash | Bank |
| | | | £ | £ | £ | | | | £ | £ | £ |
| 20-1 | | | | | | 20-1 | | | | | |
| 30 Sep | Balances b/f | | | 644 | 3,045 | 30 Sep | Nelson Stores | | | | |
| 30 Sep | Cash sales | | | 88 | | | (trade payable) | | 30 | | 1,940 |
| 30 Sep | Albany Ltd | | | | | 30 Sep | Cash purchases | | | | 192 |
| | (trade receivable) | | 25 | | 1,580 | 30 Sep | General expenses | | | 128 | |
| 30 Sep | Balance c/d | | | | 201 | 30 Sep | Wages | | | | 1,254 |
| | | | | | | 30 Sep | Office equipment | | | | 1,440 |
| | | | | | | 30 Sep | Balance c/d | | | 604 | |
| | | | 25 | 732 | 4,826 | | | | 30 | 732 | 4,826 |
| 1 Oct | Balance b/d | | | 604 | | 1 Oct | Balance b/d | | | | 201 |

**(a)** The bank balance brought forward of £3,045 on 30 September shows that, according to the cash book, the business has money in the bank. True or false?

**(b)** The bank balance brought down of £201 on 1 October shows that, according to the cash book, the business has money in the bank. True or false?

**(c)** You are to transfer the data from the cash book into the general ledger of Wentworths. Note that a bank control account is not required.

**(d)** Show the entries in the sales ledger and purchases ledger of Wentworths.

**Note:** Wentworth's business is not registered for Value Added Tax.

**9.5**   The balances in Sally Henshaw's three column cash book at 3 August 20-7 were as follows:

|  | £ |
|---|---|
| Cash in hand | 286 |
| Bank overdraft | 3,472 |

The following transactions took place

| 3 Aug | Paid rent by cheque £760 |
|---|---|
| 4 Aug | Sales £334, cash received |
| 5 Aug | Received a cheque of £1,475 from Murphy Ltd in full settlement of a debt of £1,490 |
| 8 Aug | Paid rates by direct debit £223 |
| 8 Aug | Paid JJ Supplies by cheque £490 after deducting £10 cash discount |
| 10 Aug | Drawings, £400 by cheque, made by Sally Henshaw |
| 10 Aug | Paid wages £480 in cash |

**Required:**
- Enter the above transactions in the cash book on the next page.
- Balance the cash and bank columns at 10 August 20-7, and bring the balances down on 11 August 20-7.
- Total the discount columns.

**Note:** Sally Henshaw's business is not registered for Value Added Tax.

**Cash Book**

| Dr | | | | | | | | | | | | Cr |
|---|---|---|---|---|---|---|---|---|---|---|---|---|
| Date 20-7 | Details | Discount £ | Cash £ | Bank £ | | Date 20-7 | Details | Discount £ | Cash £ | Bank £ | | |
| | | | | | | | | | | | | |
| | | | | | | | | | | | | |
| | | | | | | | | | | | | |
| | | | | | | | | | | | | |
| | | | | | | | | | | | | |
| | | | | | | | | | | | | |
| | | | | | | | | | | | | |
| | | | | | | | | | | | | |
| | | | | | | | | | | | | |
| | | | | | | | | | | | | |
| | | | | | | | | | | | | |

**9.6** Emma Maxwell uses a three column cash book as part of her double-entry bookkeeping system. The following details relate to March 20-3.

| March | | £ |
|---|---|---|
| 1 | Balance in cash account | 200 |
| | Overdrawn bank balance | 1,898 |
| 2 | Bank payment made to Lindum Supplies in settlement of an invoice for £260 | 254 |
| 6 | Cheque from Court Ltd paid into bank | 1,236 |
| 11 | Paid rent by cheque | 550 |
| 13 | BACS transfer received from H Sweeney. Discount of £10 had been taken by the customer | 1,696 |
| 14 | Sales, cash received | 639 |
| 23 | Paid wages in cash | 655 |
| 24 | Sales, cash received | 786 |
| 26 | Standing order to Wyvern Council | 195 |
| 27 | Interest charged by bank | 45 |
| 28 | BACS transfer received from Mills and Co Ltd | 477 |

**Required:**

- Enter the above transactions in the cash book shown on the next page.

- Balance the cash book at the end of the month and bring down the balances at 1 April 20-3.

- Post the discounts to the general ledger accounts shown on the next page.

**Note:** Emma Maxwell's business is not registered for Value Added Tax.

| Dr | | | | | Emma Maxwell Cash Book | | | | Cr |
|---|---|---|---|---|---|---|---|---|---|
| Date 20-3 | Details | Discount £ | Cash £ | Bank £ | Date 20-3 | Details | Discount £ | Cash £ | Bank £ |
| | | | | | | | | | |
| | | | | | | | | | |

| Dr | | | Discount Allowed Account | | | Cr |
|---|---|---|---|---|---|---|
| Date 20-3 | Details | £ | Date 20-3 | Details | £ | |
| | | | | | | |

| Dr | | | Discount Received Account | | | Cr |
|---|---|---|---|---|---|---|
| Date 20-3 | Details | £ | Date 20-3 | Details | £ | |
| | | | | | | |

# 10 Analysed cash book

**10.1** Which **ONE** of the following transactions will be recorded on the receipts side of cash book?

| | ✔ |
|---|---|
| Bank charges for £55 | |
| Payment of VAT to HM Revenue & Customs for £1,820 | |
| BACS transfer from a trade receivable for £1,950 | |
| Drawings made by the owner of the business for £750 | |

**10.2** Which **ONE** of the following transactions will be recorded on the payments side of cash book?

| | ✔ |
|---|---|
| Repayment of VAT by HM Revenue & Customs for £255 | |
| BACS transfer from a trade receivable for £690 | |
| Debit card payment to a trade payable for £940 | |
| Increase in owner's capital by bank transfer for £5,000 | |

**10.3** Show whether the following statements are true or false.

| Statement | | True ✔ | False ✔ |
|---|---|---|---|
| (a) | Cash and bank control accounts are the general ledger accounts when cash book is used as a book of prime entry only | | |
| (b) | The purchases ledger column total from cash book is credited to purchases ledger control account in general ledger | | |
| (c) | The discount allowed column total from cash book is credited to discount allowed account in general ledger | | |
| (d) | The VAT column total on the payments side of cash book is debited to VAT account in general ledger | | |

**10.4**   You are an accounts assistant at Denison Limited. One of your duties is to write-up the cash book. There are five payments to be entered in Denison Limited's cash book.

**Receipts for cash payments**

| Received cash with thanks for goods bought. | |
| --- | --- |
| From Denison Ltd, a customer without a credit account. | |
| Net | £40 |
| VAT | £8 |
| Total | £48 |
| *Clark & Co* | |

| Received cash with thanks for goods bought. | |
| --- | --- |
| From Denison Ltd, a customer without a credit account. | |
| Net | £160 |
| VAT | £32 |
| Total | £192 |
| *T Kinnear* | |

**Bank payments**

Gaskin Ltd

(Purchases ledger account PL110)

£1,690

Note: £15 settlement (cash) discount taken

Bristow Stationery

(No credit account with this supplier)

£144  including VAT

Roussouw & Co

(Purchases ledger account PL280)

£1,140

Note: no settlement (cash) discount taken

**(a)**    Enter the details from the two receipts for cash payments and the three bank payments into the credit side of the cash book shown below and total each column.

**Cash book – credit side**

| Details | Discount £ | Cash £ | Bank £ | VAT £ | Trade payables £ | Cash purchases £ | Stationery expenses £ |
|---|---|---|---|---|---|---|---|
| Balance b/f | | | | | | | |
| Clark & Co | | | | | | | |
| T Kinnear | | | | | | | |
| Gaskin Ltd | | | | | | | |
| Bristow Stationery | | | | | | | |
| Roussouw & Co | | | | | | | |
| Totals | | | | | | | |

There are two bank receipts from credit customers to be entered in Denison Limited's cash book:

Passmores  £455

S McNulty   £833  Note: £15 settlement (cash) discount taken

**(b)**    Enter the above details into the debit side of the cash book and total each column.

**Cash book – debit side**

| Details | Discount £ | Cash £ | Bank £ | Trade receivables £ |
|---|---|---|---|---|
| Balance b/f | | 642 | 1,022 | |
| Passmores | | | | |
| S McNulty | | | | |
| Totals | | | | |

**(c)** Using your answers to (a) and (b) above, calculate the cash balance.

£

**(d)** Using your answers to (a) and (b) above, calculate the bank balance.

£

**(e)** Will the bank balance calculated in (d) above be a debit or credit balance?

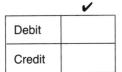

| Debit | |
| --- | --- |
| Credit | |

**10.5** There are four payments to be entered in Rowson Limited's cash book.

Payments to suppliers who do not offer credit accounts:

- cash paid to Mary Wallbank of £192, including VAT, for goods purchased
- a bank payment of £425, no VAT, to Wenton Council for rates

Payments to credit suppliers:

- BACS payments made as authorised on the two invoices shown below.

| Sanders plc |
| --- |
| 2 Albany Road |
| Wenton WT4 8PQ |
| VAT Registration No 208 7641 00 |

| Invoice No. 6231 | 30 June 20-4 |
| --- | --- |

To: Rowson Ltd
   14 Blenheim Road
   Wenton, WT2 1XJ

| | £ |
| --- | --- |
| 50 items of AB @ £10.00 each | 500.00 |
| VAT @ 20% | 98.00 |
| Total | 598.00 |

Authorised for payment of £588, £10 settlement discount taken: T Rowson

*Terms: 2% settlement discount for payment in 10 days or 30 days net.*

| J.Panas |
| --- |
| Market Street |
| South Wenton WT6 4JK |
| VAT Registration No 396 4918 00 |

| Invoice No. I2721 | 30 June 20-4 |
| --- | --- |

To: Rowson Ltd
   14 Blenheim Road
   Wenton, WT2 1XJ

| | £ |
| --- | --- |
| 80 items of AD @ £7.00 each | 560.00 |
| VAT @ 20% | 112.00 |
| Total | 672.00 |

Authorised for payment in full: T Rowson

*Terms: 30 days net.*

**(a)** Enter the details of the four payments into the credit side of the cash book shown below and total each column.

**Cash book – credit side**

| Details | Discount £ | Cash £ | Bank £ | VAT £ | Trade payables £ | Cash purchases £ | Other expenses £ |
|---|---|---|---|---|---|---|---|
| Balance b/f | | | 2,417 | | | | |
| | | | | | | | |
| | | | | | | | |
| | | | | | | | |
| | | | | | | | |
| **Totals** | | | | | | | |

There are three amounts received to be entered in Rowson Limited's cash book.

Cheques received from credit customers:

- LFJ plc £1,685
- Wragg Ltd £2,135 (this customer has taken a £20 settlement discount)

Cash received:

- £200 received from Nikki Shah for rent of office space (No VAT)

**(b)** Enter the details of the three receipts into the debit side of the cash book shown below and total each column.

**Cash book – debit side**

| Details | Discount £ | Cash £ | Bank £ | Trade receivables £ | Other income £ |
|---|---|---|---|---|---|
| Balance b/f | | 208 | | | |
| | | | | | |
| | | | | | |
| | | | | | |
| **Totals** | | | | | |

**(c)**   Using your answers to (a) and (b) on the previous page, calculate the cash balance.

£ [                    ]

**(d)**   Using your answers to (a) and (b) on the previous page, calculate the bank balance. If your calculations show that the bank account is overdrawn your answer should start with a minus sign, for example –123.

£ [                    ]

**(e)**   What will be the entry in Sanders plc's account in the purchases ledger to record the discount received?

**Purchases ledger**

| Account name | Amount £ | Debit ✔ | Credit ✔ |
|---|---|---|---|
| Sanders plc | | | |

# 11 Petty cash book

**11.1** The imprest system for petty cash means that:

| | ✔ |
|---|---|
| Petty cash payments up to a stated amount can be authorised by the petty cashier | |
| Petty cash vouchers must have relevant documentation attached | |
| The petty cash float is restored to the same amount for the beginning of each week or month | |
| Petty cash vouchers are numbered and the number is recorded in the petty cash book | |

**11.2** A petty cash control account has a balance b/d of £150 at the beginning of a month. During the month, payments are made from petty cash which total £108. Which **ONE** of the following transactions will restore the balance of petty cash control account to £150?

| | ✔ |
|---|---|
| Debit bank £150; credit petty cash control £150 | |
| Debit petty cash control £108; credit bank £108 | |
| Debit petty cash control £42; credit bank £42 | |
| Debit bank £108; credit petty cash control £108 | |

**11.3** Show whether the following statements are true or false.

| Statement | True ✔ | False ✔ |
|---|---|---|
| Payments are recorded on the debit side of petty cash book | | |
| A petty cash book may combine the roles of a book of prime entry and double-entry bookkeeping | | |
| Petty cash vouchers are authorised for payment by the petty cashier | | |
| The totals of the petty cash analysis columns are transferred to general ledger where they are debited to the appropriate expense account | | |

**11.4**  A firm's petty cash book is operated on the imprest system. The imprest amount is £250. At the end of a particular period, the analysis columns are totalled as follows: VAT £13.42; postage £29.18; travel £45.47; stationery £33.29; cleaning £18.54.

How much cash will be required to restore the imprest amount for the next period?

| | ✔ |
|---|---|
| £250.00 | |
| £126.48 | |
| £139.90 | |
| £110.10 | |

**11.5**  A firm's petty cash book is operated on the imprest system. The imprest amount is £125. At the end of a particular period the petty cash remaining comprised:

2 x £10 notes, 5 x £5 notes, 4 x £1 coins, 3 x 50p coins, 6 x 20p coins, 3 x 10p coins, 3 x 5p coins, 8 x 1p coins.

Provided no errors or discrepancies have occurred, what is the amount of payments that will be recorded in the petty cash book for the period?

| | ✔ |
|---|---|
| £72.77 | |
| £52.23 | |
| £72.65 | |
| £125.00 | |

**11.6**  The petty cashier of the business where you work tops up the petty cash at the end of the month with £110 withdrawn from the bank.

What will be the entries in the general ledger?

Select your account names from the following list: Bank, Cash, Petty cash book, Purchases, Purchases ledger control, Sales, Sales ledger control, Value Added Tax.

**General ledger**

| Account name | Amount £ | Debit ✔ | Credit ✔ |
|---|---|---|---|
| | | | |
| | | | |

**11.7** Wyvern Property maintains a petty cash book as both a book of prime entry and part of the double-entry accounting system. The following transactions all took place on 30 June and have been entered in the petty cash book as shown below. No entries have yet been made in the general ledger.

**Petty cash book**

| Date 20-4 | Details | Amount £ | Date 20-4 | Details | Amount £ | VAT £ | Postage £ | Travel expenses £ | Stationery £ |
|---|---|---|---|---|---|---|---|---|---|
| 30 Jun | Balance b/f | 68.00 | 30 Jun | Taxi | 14.88 | 2.48 | | 12.40 | |
| 30 Jun | Bank | 57.00 | 30 Jun | Copy paper | 18.72 | 3.12 | | | 15.60 |
| | | | 30 Jun | Post office | 11.50 | | 11.50 | | |
| | | | 30 Jun | Rail fare | 22.35 | | | 22.35 | |
| | | | | Balance c/d | 57.55 | | | | |
| | | 125.00 | | | 125.00 | 5.60 | 11.50 | 34.75 | 15.60 |

What will be the entries in the general ledger?

Select your account names from the following list: Balance b/f, Balance c/d, Bank, Copy paper, Petty cash book, Postage, Post office, Rail fare, Stationery, Taxi, Travel expenses, Value Added Tax.

**General ledger**

| Account name | Amount £ | Debit ✔ | Credit ✔ |
|---|---|---|---|
| | | | |
| | | | |
| | | | |
| | | | |
| | | | |

**11.8** The following petty cash book shows a number of transactions of Elliotts Limited for July 20-6. The petty cash book is kept solely as a book of prime entry.

| Receipts | Date | Details | Voucher number | Total payment | VAT | Travel | Postages | Stationery | Meals | Ledger |
|---|---|---|---|---|---|---|---|---|---|---|
| **£** | 20-6 | | | **£** | **£** | **£** | **£** | **£** | **£** | **£** |
| 200.00 | 1 Jul | Balance b/f | | | | | | | | |
| | 6 Jul | Post office | 104 | 11.55 | | | 11.55 | | | |
| | 9 Jul | Rail fare | 105 | 17.60 | | 17.60 | | | | |
| | 11 Jul | Envelopes | 106 | 9.60 | 1.60 | | | 8.00 | | |
| | 12 Jul | Meal allowance | 107 | 10.00 | | | | | 10.00 | |
| 6.25 | 14 Jul | T Irwin (postage) | 582 | | | | | | | |
| | 19 Jul | Taxi | 108 | 10.08 | 1.68 | 8.40 | | | | |
| | 22 Jul | J Clarke (PL) | 109 | 18.25 | | | | | | 18.25 |
| | 25 Jul | Marker pens | 110 | 6.24 | 1.04 | | | 5.20 | | |
| | | | | 83.32 | 4.32 | 26.00 | 11.55 | 13.20 | 10.00 | 18.25 |
| 77.07 | 31 Jul | Bank | | | | | | | | |
| | 31 Jul | Balance c/d | | 200.00 | | | | | | |
| 283.32 | | | | 283.32 | | | | | | |
| 200.00 | 1 Aug | Balance b/d | | | | | | | | |

**Petty Cash Book** — PCB35

**(a)** You are to transfer the data from the petty cash book into the general ledger accounts (including cash book) as at 31 July 20-6. Note that a petty cash control is required.

**(b)** Show the entry that will be recorded in purchases ledger as at 31 July 20-6.

**11.9** This is a summary of petty cash payments made by Dalbeith & Co:

| | |
|---|---|
| Post office paid | £10.70 (no VAT) |
| City Taxis paid | £14.40 including VAT at 20% |
| Repair Shop Ltd paid | £18.80 plus VAT at 20% |

**(a)** Enter the above transactions, in the order in which they are shown, in the petty cash book below.

**(b)** Total the petty cash book and show the balance carried down.

Select your entries for the Details columns from the following list: Amount, Balance b/f, Balance c/d, City Taxis, Details, Postage, Post office, Repairs, Repair Shop Ltd, Travel, VAT.

**Petty cash book**

| Debit side | | Credit side | | | | | |
|---|---|---|---|---|---|---|---|
| Details | Amount £ | Details | Amount £ | VAT £ | Postage £ | Travel £ | Repairs £ |
| Balance b/f | 150.00 | | | | | | |
| | | | | | | | |
| | | | | | | | |
| | | | | | | | |
| | | | | | | | |

**11.10** Part way through the month, the petty cash account had a balance of £93.30. The cash in the petty cash box was checked and the following notes and coins were present.

| Notes and coins | £ |
| --- | --- |
| 4 x £10 notes | 40.00 |
| 7 x £5 notes | 35.00 |
| 9 x £1 coins | 9.00 |
| 13 x 50p coins | 6.50 |
| 10 x 10p coins | 1.00 |
| 17 x 5p coins | 0.85 |

**(a)** Reconcile the cash amount in the petty cash box with the balance on the petty cash account.

| Amount in petty cash box | £ |
| --- | --- |
| Balance on petty cash account | £ |
| Difference | £ |

At the end of the month the cash in the petty cash box was £45.65.

**(b)** Complete the petty cash reimbursement below to restore the imprest amount of £175.

| Petty cash reimbursement | |
| --- | --- |
| Date: 30.04.20-5 | |
| Amount required to restore the cash in the petty cash box | £ |

# 12 The initial trial balance

**12.1**  Which **ONE** of the following accounts always has a credit balance?

|  | ✔ |
|---|---|
| Drawings account |  |
| Sales returns account |  |
| Sales account |  |
| Office equipment account |  |

**12.2**  Which **ONE** of the following accounts always has a debit balance?

|  | ✔ |
|---|---|
| Purchases returns account |  |
| Sales ledger control account |  |
| Capital account |  |
| Loan account |  |

**12.3**  Prepare the initial trial balance of Kate Trelawney as at 31 March 20-2. She has omitted to open a capital account. **You are to** fill in the missing figure in order to balance the trial balance.

|  | £ |
|---|---|
| Bank loan | 3,650 |
| Purchases | 23,745 |
| Vehicle | 9,500 |
| Sales | 65,034 |
| Bank (cash at bank) | 2,162 |
| Discount allowed | 317 |
| Purchases returns | 855 |
| Sales ledger control | 7,045 |
| Office equipment | 5,450 |
| Inventory at 1 April 20-1 | 4,381 |
| Sales returns | 1,624 |
| Purchases ledger control | 4,736 |
| Expenses | 32,598 |
| Discount received | 494 |
| Capital | ? |

**12.4**   You work as an accounts assistant for Wyvern Trading. The accounts supervisor has asked you to work on preparing an initial trial balance as at 31 December 20-8. The supervisor has given you the following list of balances to be transferred to the trial balance.

**You are to** place the figures in the debit or credit column, as appropriate, and to total each column.

| Account name | Amount £ | Debit £ | Credit £ |
|---|---|---|---|
| Bank (overdraft) | 4,293 | | |
| Loan from bank | 12,500 | | |
| Vehicles | 25,500 | | |
| Inventory | 10,417 | | |
| Petty cash control | 68 | | |
| Capital | 25,794 | | |
| VAT owing to HM Revenue & Customs | 1,496 | | |
| Purchases ledger control | 12,794 | | |
| Purchases | 104,763 | | |
| Purchases returns | 2,681 | | |
| Sales ledger control | 28,354 | | |
| Sales | 184,267 | | |
| Sales returns | 4,098 | | |
| Discount allowed | 1,312 | | |
| Discount received | 1,784 | | |
| Wages | 35,961 | | |
| Telephone | 3,474 | | |
| Advertising | 5,921 | | |
| Insurance | 3,084 | | |
| Heating and lighting | 2,477 | | |
| Rent and rates | 3,672 | | |
| Postages | 876 | | |
| Miscellaneous expenses | 545 | | |
| Drawings | 15,087 | | |
| Totals | – | | |

**12.5** You work as an accounts assistant for Highley Limited. The accounts supervisor has asked you to work on preparing an initial trial balance as at 30 June 20-1. The supervisor has given you the following list of balances to be transferred to the trial balance.

**You are to** place the figures in the debit or credit column, as appropriate, and to total each column.

| Account name | Amount £ | Debit £ | Credit £ |
|---|---|---|---|
| Sales | 262,394 | | |
| Sales returns | 2,107 | | |
| Sales ledger control | 33,844 | | |
| Purchases | 157,988 | | |
| Purchases returns | 1,745 | | |
| Purchases ledger control | 17,311 | | |
| Discount received | 1,297 | | |
| Discount allowed | 845 | | |
| Rent and rates | 5,941 | | |
| Advertising | 6,088 | | |
| Insurance | 3,176 | | |
| Wages | 48,954 | | |
| Heating and lighting | 4,266 | | |
| Postages and telephone | 2,107 | | |
| Miscellaneous expenses | 632 | | |
| Vehicles | 28,400 | | |
| Capital | 48,756 | | |
| Drawings | 19,354 | | |
| Office equipment | 10,500 | | |
| Inventory | 16,246 | | |
| Petty cash control | 150 | | |
| Bank (cash at bank) | 3,096 | | |
| VAT owing to HM Revenue & Customs | 3,721 | | |
| Loan from bank | 8,470 | | |
| Totals | – | | |

**12.6** It is important to understand the difference between capital expenditure, revenue expenditure, capital income and revenue income.

Select **ONE** option in each instance below to show whether the item will be capital expenditure, revenue expenditure, capital income or revenue income.

| Item | Capital expenditure ✔ | Revenue expenditure ✔ | Capital income ✔ | Revenue income ✔ |
|---|---|---|---|---|
| Purchase of vehicles | | | | |
| Fuel for vehicles | | | | |
| Discounts received | | | | |
| Receipts from sale of office equipment | | | | |
| Redecoration of property | | | | |
| Extension to property | | | | |
| Receipts from sale of goods to credit customers | | | | |
| Delivery cost of new machine | | | | |
| Increase in owner's capital | | | | |
| Repairs to vehicles | | | | |

# Chapter activities
# answers

# 1 The accounting system

**1.1**   Cash sale

**1.2**   The first place an entry is recorded in the accounting records

**1.3**   Cash and credit and other financial transactions

**1.4**   Customers who buy goods and services on a credit basis

**1.5**   A *trial balance* sets out in two columns the balances of the *ledger accounts* of a business. The *totals* of the two columns should *agree*. The debit column includes the accounts of *receivables* and the credit column includes the accounts of *payables*. This provides the *managers* of a business with important and useful financial information.

# 2 Financial documents for sales

**2.1**   **(a)**

---

**INVOICE**                                        **No** 1689

**PRAXIS STATIONERY**                    **Date** 09 07 20-3
45 Jarvis Street
Mereford MR1 2GH
VAT Reg 831 8627 06

To
Dover Designs
68 Whitecliff Street, Granstow, GR3 7GH

Customer code   DO109

Delivery note no  246

| Quantity | Product code | Unit price (£) | Total (£) | Net (£) | VAT (£) | Total (£) |
|---|---|---|---|---|---|---|
| 100 | BX100 | 4.00 | 400.00 | 320.00 | 62.72 | 382.72 |

**(b)**    £382.72

2.2

| STATEMENT OF ACCOUNT<br>**PRAXIS STATIONERY**<br>45 Jarvis Street, Mereford MR1 2GH | | **To** Rosetti Associates<br>**Date** 31 08 20-3 | |
|---|---|---|---|
| **Date** | **Details** | **Amount £** | **Balance outstanding £** |
| 1 August | Invoice 1748 | 4,567.89 | 4,567.89 |
| 9 August | Invoice 1778 | 2,457.60 | 7,025.49 |
| 10 August | Invoice 1783 | 4,678.30 | 11,703.79 |
| 17 August | Credit note 319 | 280.50 | 11,423.29 |
| 29 August | Cheque | 4,287.39 | 7,135.90 |

2.3

| **Product** | **Customer** | **General Ledger Code** | **Customer Code** |
|---|---|---|---|
| Copy paper | Britmore Ltd | GL4002 | BRI45 |
| Gel pens | Coldring Limited | GL4003 | COL12 |
| Box files | Artex Limited | GL4018 | ART09 |
| Black printer ink | Coleman Trading | GL4017 | COL10 |
| Archive storage boxes | Bristol Wholesale | GL4008 | BRI25 |
| Suspension files | Britmore Limited | GL4018 | BRI45 |

2.4    A credit note

2.5    **(a)**    £121.60

      **(b)**    £761.60

# 3 Double-entry and the accounting equation

**3.1** In the ledgers

**3.2** Purchases ledger

**3.3**

|  | Debit | Credit |
|---|---|---|
| Money paid for **Purchases** | Purchases | Bank |
| Money received from **Sales** | Bank | Sales |
| **Rent paid** for premises used | Rent paid | Bank |
| **Rent received** for premises let | Bank | Rent received |
| **Motor expenses** paid | Motor expenses | Bank |
| Payment for **advertising** costs | Advertising | Bank |
| **Stationery** bill paid | Stationery | Bank |
| **Loan** received | Bank | Loan |
| **Loan** repayment made | Loan | Bank |

**3.4**

| Debit | | | Sales Account | | | Credit |
|---|---|---|---|---|---|---|
| Date | Details | £ | Date | Details | | £ |
|  |  |  | 1 Feb | Bank | | 5,000 |
|  |  |  | 2 Feb | Bank | | 7,500 |
|  |  |  | 5 Feb | Bank | | 9,300 |

| Debit | | | Purchases Account | | | Credit |
|---|---|---|---|---|---|---|
| Date | Details | £ | Date | Details | | £ |
| 1 Feb | Bank | 3,500 |  |  | |  |
| 3 Feb | Bank | 5,000 |  |  | |  |

| Debit | | | Wages Account | | | Credit |
|---|---|---|---|---|---|---|
| Date | Details | £ | Date | Details | | £ |
| 2 Feb | Bank | 2,510 | | | | |

| Debit | | | Rent Paid Account | | | Credit |
|---|---|---|---|---|---|---|
| Date | Details | £ | Date | Details | | £ |
| 4 Feb | Bank | 780 | | | | |

| Debit | | | Bank Loan Account | | | Credit |
|---|---|---|---|---|---|---|
| Date | Details | £ | Date | Details | | £ |
| | | | 3 Feb | Bank | | 12,500 |

**3.5**

**(a)**

| Statement | True | False |
|---|---|---|
| Liabilities equals capital plus assets | | ✔ |
| Assets equals liabilities minus capital | | ✔ |
| Capital equals assets minus liabilities | ✔ | |

**(b)**

| Item | Asset | Liability |
|------|:-----:|:---------:|
| Vehicles | | ✔ |
| Bank loan | | ✔ |
| Money owing by trade receivables | ✔ | |
| Inventory | ✔ | |
| Cash | | ✔ |
| VAT owing to HM Revenue & Customs | | ✔ |

**3.6**

| Assets | Liabilities | Capital |
|:------:|:-----------:|:-------:|
| £ | £ | £ |
| 50,000 | 0 | 50,000 |
| 40,000 | 10,000 | 30,000 |
| 55,200 | 24,950 | 30,250 |
| 58,980 | 18,220 | 40,760 |
| 40,320 | 15,980 | 24,340 |
| 73,350 | 24,760 | 48,590 |

**3.7**

| Transaction | Debit | Credit |
|-------------|:-----:|:------:|
| Capital account increases | | ✔ |
| Liability account increases | | ✔ |
| Asset account decreases | | ✔ |
| Liability account decreases | ✔ | |
| Asset account increases | ✔ | |

**3.8**

(a) - (b)    Vehicles have been bought for £10,000, paid from the bank

(b) - (c)    Inventory has been bought for £6,000, paid from the bank

(c) - (d)    Inventory has been bought for £3,000, on credit from a supplier

(d) - (e)    Further vehicle bought for £8,000, paid for with £3,000 from the bank and a loan for £5,000

(e) - (f)    Owner introduces £10,000 additional capital, paid into the bank

**3.9**

| Dr | | | Bank | | | Cr |
|---|---|---|---|---|---|---|
| **20-4** | **Details** | **£** | **20-4** | **Details** | | **£** |
| 4 March | Capital | 5,000 | 11 March | Purchases | | 375 |
| 5 March | Bank loan | 15,000 | 15 March | Rent | | 400 |
| 7 March | Sales | 670 | 16 March | Purchases | | 1,380 |
| 18 March | Sales | 430 | 22 March | Telephone | | 180 |
| 26 March | Sales | 1,320 | 29 March | Insurance | | 1,200 |

| Account | Date | Dr or Cr | Details | Amount £ |
|---|---|---|---|---|
| Capital | 4 March | Cr | Bank | 5,000 |
| Bank loan | 5 March | Cr | Bank | 15,000 |
| Sales | 7 March | Cr | Bank | 670 |
| Purchases | 11 March | Dr | Bank | 375 |
| Rent | 15 March | Dr | Bank | 400 |
| Purchases | 16 March | Dr | Bank | 1,380 |
| Sales | 18 March | Cr | Bank | 430 |
| Telephone | 22 March | Dr | Bank | 180 |
| Sales | 26 March | Cr | Bank | 1,320 |
| Insurance | 29 March | Dr | Bank | 1,200 |

**3.10**

**(a)**

| Dr | | | Egret Building (Sales Ledger) | | | Cr |
|---|---|---|---|---|---|---|
| **20-4** | **Details** | **£** | **20-4** | **Details** | | **£** |
| 24 Aug | Sales | 900.00 | 25 Aug | Sales returns | | 160.00 |
| 27 Aug | Sales | 140.00 | 31 Aug | Balance c/d | | 1,240.00 |
| 28 Aug | Sales | 360.00 | | | | |
| | | 1,400.00 | | | | 1,400.00 |
| 1 Sep | Balance b/d | 1,240.00 | | | | |

**(b)**

| Dr | | | Curtis & Curtis (Purchases Ledger) | | | Cr |
|---|---|---|---|---|---|---|
| **20-4** | **Details** | **£** | **20-4** | **Details** | | **£** |
| 31 Aug | Balance c/d | 1,013.50 | 24 Aug | Purchases | | 496.00 |
| | | | 26 Aug | Purchases | | 157.50 |
| | | | 31 Aug | Purchases | | 360.00 |
| | | 1,013.50 | | | | 1,013.50 |
| | | | 1 Sep | Balance b/d | | 1,013.50 |

**(c)**

| Dr | R & T Engineering (Purchases Ledger) | | | Cr | |
|---|---|---|---|---|---|
| **20-4** | **Details** | **£** | **20-4** | **Details** | **£** |
| 24 Aug | Purchases returns | 160.00 | 25 Aug | Purchases | 240.00 |
| 31 Aug | Balance c/d | 1,140.00 | 28 Aug | Purchases | 720.00 |
| | | | 31 Aug | Purchases | 340.00 |
| | | 1,300.00 | | | 1,300.00 |
| | | | 1 Sep | Balance b/d | 1,140.00 |

**(d)**

| Dr | Motor expenses (General Ledger) | | | Cr | |
|---|---|---|---|---|---|
| **20-4** | **Details** | **£** | **20-4** | **Details** | **£** |
| 5 Aug | Bank | 150.40 | 31 Aug | Balance c/d | 728.60 |
| 7 Aug | Bank | 382.00 | | | |
| 9 Aug | Bank | 69.30 | | | |
| 16 Aug | Bank | 126.90 | | | |
| | | 728.60 | | | 728.60 |
| 1 Sep | Balance b/d | 728.60 | | | |

# 4 Accounting for sales and sales returns

**4.1** Sales invoice

**4.2** Credit note issued; sales returns day book; sales returns account; sales ledger control account; customer's account

**4.3** Credit note

**4.4** (a)

| Sales Day Book | | | | | | SDB65 |
|---|---|---|---|---|---|---|
| **Date** | **Details** | **Invoice number** | **Account code** | **Total** | **VAT** | **Net** |
| **20-4** | | | | £ | £ | £ |
| 3 Nov | Dines Stores | 3592 | SL086 | 318.00 | 53.00 | 265.00 |
| 5 Nov | Raven Retailers Ltd | 3593 | SL170 | 402.00 | 67.00 | 335.00 |
| 6 Nov | Meadow Golf Club | 3594 | SL135 | 210.00 | 35.00 | 175.00 |
| 10 Nov | Wyvern Stores | 3595 | SL195 | 546.00 | 91.00 | 455.00 |
| 11 Nov | Dines Stores | 3596 | SL086 | 348.00 | 58.00 | 290.00 |
| 13 Nov | Teme Sports Ltd | 3597 | SL178 | 378.00 | 63.00 | 315.00 |
| 17 Nov | Raven Retailers Ltd | 3598 | SL170 | 1,344.00 | 224.00 | 1,120.00 |
| 19 Nov | Teme Sports Ltd | 3599 | SL178 | 990.00 | 165.00 | 825.00 |
| 21 Nov | Dines Stores | 3600 | SL086 | 424.80 | 70.80 | 354.00 |
| 24 Nov | Meadow Golf Club | 3601 | SL135 | 297.60 | 49.60 | 248.00 |
| 27 Nov | Wyvern Stores | 3602 | SL195 | 627.60 | 104.60 | 523.00 |
| 30 Nov | Totals for month | | | 5,886.00 | 981.00 | 4,905.00 |
| | | | | GL1200 | GL2200 | GL4100 |

**(b)**

## GENERAL LEDGER

| Dr | | | Sales Ledger Control Account (GL1200) | | | Cr |
|---|---|---|---|---|---|---|
| 20-4 | | | £ | 20-4 | | £ |
| 30 Nov | Sales Day Book SDB65 | | 5,886.00 | | | |

| Dr | | | Value Added Tax Account (GL2200) | | | Cr |
|---|---|---|---|---|---|---|
| 20-4 | | | £ | 20-4 | | £ |
| | | | | 30 Nov | Sales Day Book SDB65 | 981.00 |

| Dr | | | Sales Account (GL4100) | | | Cr |
|---|---|---|---|---|---|---|
| 20-4 | | | £ | 20-4 | | £ |
| | | | | 30 Nov | Sales Day Book SDB65 | 4,905.00 |

## SALES LEDGER

| Dr | | | Dines Stores (SL086) | | Cr |
|---|---|---|---|---|---|
| 20-4 | | | £ | 20-4 | £ |
| 3 Nov | Sales | SDB65 | 318.00 | | |
| 11 Nov | Sales | SDB65 | 348.00 | | |
| 21 Nov | Sales | SDB65 | 424.80 | | |

| Dr | | | Meadow Golf Club (SL135) | | Cr |
|---|---|---|---|---|---|
| 20-4 | | | £ | 20-4 | £ |
| 6 Nov | Sales | SDB65 | 210.00 | | |
| 24 Nov | Sales | SDB65 | 297.60 | | |

| Dr | | | Raven Retailers Limited (SL170) | | Cr |
|---|---|---|---|---|---|
| 20-4 | | | £ | 20-4 | £ |
| 5 Nov | Sales | SDB65 | 402.00 | | |
| 17 Nov | Sales | SDB65 | 1,344.00 | | |

| Dr | | | Teme Sports Limited (SL178) | | Cr |
|---|---|---|---|---|---|
| 20-4 | | | £ | 20-4 | £ |
| 13 Nov | Sales | SDB65 | 378.00 | | |
| 19 Nov | Sales | SDB65 | 990.00 | | |

| Dr | | | Wyvern Stores (SL195) | | Cr |
|---|---|---|---|---|---|
| 20-4 | | | £ | 20-4 | £ |
| 10 Nov | Sales | SDB65 | 546.00 | | |
| 27 Nov | Sales | SDB65 | 627.60 | | |

**4.5** **(a)**

| Date | Details | Credit note number | Account code | Total | VAT | Net |
|---|---|---|---|---|---|---|
| | | | **Sales Returns Day Book** | | | **SRDB22** |
| **20-4** | | | | £ | £ | £ |
| 10 Nov | Dines Stores | 831 | SL086 | 66.00 | 11.00 | 55.00 |
| 14 Nov | Wyvern Stores | 832 | SL195 | 72.00 | 12.00 | 60.00 |
| 19 Nov | Meadow Golf Club | 833 | SL135 | 55.20 | 9.20 | 46.00 |
| 24 Nov | Teme Sports Ltd | 834 | SL178 | 152.40 | 25.40 | 127.00 |
| 28 Nov | Dines Stores | 835 | SL086 | 104.40 | 17.40 | 87.00 |
| 30 Nov | Totals for month | | | 450.00 | 75.00 | 375.00 |
| | | | | GL1200 | GL2200 | GL4110 |

**(b)** **GENERAL LEDGER**

Dr               **Sales Ledger Control Account** (GL1200)           Cr

| 20-4 | £ | 20-4 | £ |
|---|---|---|---|
| 30 Nov Sales Day Book    SDB65 | 5,886.00 | 30 Nov  Sales Returns Day Book    SRDB22 | 450.00 |

Dr               **Value Added Tax Account** (GL2200)           Cr

| 20-4 | £ | 20-4 | £ |
|---|---|---|---|
| 30 Nov  Sales Returns Day Book    SRDB22 | 75.00 | 30 Nov  Sales Day Book SDB65 | 981.00 |

Dr               **Sales Returns Account** (GL4110)           Cr

| 20-4 | £ | 20-4 | £ |
|---|---|---|---|
| 30 Nov  Sales Returns Day Book    SRDB22 | 375.00 | | |

**SALES LEDGER**

| Dr | | Dines Stores (SL086) | | | Cr |
|---|---|---|---|---|---|
| 20-4 | | £ | 20-4 | | £ |
| 3 Nov Sales | SDB65 | 318.00 | 10 Nov Sales Returns | SRDB22 | 66.00 |
| 11 Nov Sales | SDB65 | 348.00 | 28 Nov Sales Returns | SRDB22 | 104.40 |
| 21 Nov Sales | SDB65 | 424.80 | | | |

| Dr | | Meadow Golf Club (SL135) | | | Cr |
|---|---|---|---|---|---|
| 20-4 | | £ | 20-4 | | £ |
| 6 Nov Sales | SDB65 | 210.00 | 19 Nov Sales Returns | SRDB22 | 55.20 |
| 24 Nov Sales | SDB65 | 297.60 | | | |

| Dr | | Teme Sports Limited (SL178) | | | Cr |
|---|---|---|---|---|---|
| 20-4 | | £ | 20-4 | | £ |
| 13 Nov Sales | SDB65 | 378.00 | 24 Nov Sales Returns | SRDB22 | 152.40 |
| 19 Nov Sales | SDB65 | 990.00 | | | |

| Dr | | Wyvern Stores (SL195) | | | Cr |
|---|---|---|---|---|---|
| 20-4 | | £ | 20-4 | | £ |
| 10 Nov Sales | SDB65 | 546.00 | 14 Nov Sales Returns | SRDB22 | 72.00 |
| 27 Nov Sales | SDB65 | 627.60 | | | |

**4.6    (a) and (b)**

**Sales day book**

| Date 20-4 | Details | Invoice number | Total £ | VAT £ | Net £ | Sales type 1 £ | Sales type 2 £ |
|---|---|---|---|---|---|---|---|
| 30 June | Olander Ltd | 1895 | 1,920 | 320 | 1,600 | 1,600 | |
| 30 June | Boltz & Co | 1896 | 5,040 | 840 | 4,200 | | 4,200 |
| 30 June | Ravells | 1897 | 576 | 96 | 480 | 480 | |
| | **Totals** | | 7,536 | 1,256 | 6,280 | 2,080 | 4,200 |

**4.7** **(a)**

**Sales ledger**

| Account name | Amount £ | Debit | Credit |
|---|---|---|---|
| Upton Ltd | 2,016 | ✔ | |
| Bromyards | 3,408 | ✔ | |
| Kempsey & Co | 4,272 | ✔ | |
| Fernhill plc | 2,448 | ✔ | |

**General ledger**

| Account name | Amount £ | Debit | Credit |
|---|---|---|---|
| Sales | 10,120 | | ✔ |
| Value Added Tax | 2,024 | | ✔ |
| Sales ledger control | 12,144 | ✔ | |

**(b)**

**Sales ledger**

| Account name | Amount £ | Debit | Credit |
|---|---|---|---|
| Drake & Co | 336 | | ✔ |
| Hanbury Trading | 1,008 | | ✔ |

**General ledger**

| Account name | Amount £ | Debit | Credit |
|---|---|---|---|
| Sales returns | 1,120 | ✔ | |
| Value Added Tax | 224 | ✔ | |
| Sales ledger control | 1,344 | | ✔ |

**4.8**

**Sales day book**

| Date 20-4 | Details | Invoice number | Total £ | VAT £ | Net £ | Product S12 £ | Product T12 £ |
|---|---|---|---|---|---|---|---|
| 30 June | Hawke Ltd | 2132 | 360.00 | 60.00 | 300.00 | | 300.00 |
| 30 June | T Martin | 2133 | 450.00 | 75.00 | 375.00 | 375.00 | |
| 30 June | S Garner | 2134 | 630.00 | 105.00 | 525.00 | 525.00 | |
| 30 June | JEC Ltd | 2135 | 180.00 | 30.00 | 150.00 | | 150.00 |
| | **Totals** | | 1,620.00 | 270.00 | 1,350.00 | 900.00 | 450.00 |

# 5 Process payments from customers

**5.1**   Sales documention reference numbers

**5.2**   Same amount in words and figures, in date, signature of customer

**5.3**   **(a)**   Invoice 392 is for £690 and not for £590

**(b)**   Credit note 295 for £90 has not been allowed for on the remittance advice

# 6    Process documents from suppliers

**6.1**    Delivery note

**6.2**    The purchases ledger

**6.3**    Purchases

**6.4**

**(a)**    Who has supplied the chairs?

> Helicon Furniture

**(b)**    What is the problem with the consignment?

> 2 chairs damaged

**(c)**    What document would be issued by the supplier to adjust the account of Praxis Stationery?

> credit note

**(d)**    Where in the supplier's accounting records would the account of Praxis Stationery be maintained?

> sales ledger

**6.5** Has the correct purchase price of the chairs been charged? Yes or No?

YES

Has the correct discount been applied? Yes or No?

NO

What would be the VAT amount charged if the invoice was correct?

£288.00

What would be the total amount charged if the invoice was correct?

£1,728.00

**6.6** Has the correct number of tables been supplied? Yes or No?

NO

Has the correct type of table been supplied? Yes or No?

NO

What will be the total of the invoice on the basis of the details on the delivery note?

£384.00

If a credit note were issued, what would be the total, including VAT?

£76.80

# 7 Accounting for purchases and purchases returns

**7.1** Purchases invoice

**7.2** Invoice received; purchases day book; purchases account; purchases ledger control account; supplier's account

**7.3** Debit purchases; debit VAT; credit purchases ledger control

**7.4** **(a)**

| Purchases Day Book | | | | | | PDB55 |
|---|---|---|---|---|---|---|
| **Date** | **Details** | **Invoice number** | **Account code** | **Total** | **VAT** | **Net** |
| **20-2** | | | | £ | £ | £ |
| 3 May | Malvern Manufacturing | 7321 | PL625 | 204.00 | 34.00 | 170.00 |
| 9 May | S Burston | SB745 | PL530 | 318.00 | 53.00 | 265.00 |
| 12 May | Iley Supplies Ltd | 4721 | PL605 | 540.00 | 90.00 | 450.00 |
| 18 May | SG Enterprises | 3947 | PL720 | 990.00 | 165.00 | 825.00 |
| 23 May | S Burston | SB773 | PL530 | 512.40 | 85.40 | 427.00 |
| 30 May | Malvern Manufacturing | 7408 | PL625 | 436.80 | 72.80 | 364.00 |
| 31 May | Totals for month | | | 3,001.20 | 500.20 | 2,501.00 |
| | | | | GL2350 | GL2200 | GL5100 |

**(b)**                                 **GENERAL LEDGER**

| Dr | | Value Added Tax Account (GL2200) | | | Cr |
|---|---|---|---|---|---|
| 20-2 | | £ | 20-2 | | £ |
| 31 May Purchases Day Book | PDB55 | 500.20 | | | |

| Dr | | Purchases Ledger Control Account (GL2350) | | | Cr |
|---|---|---|---|---|---|
| 20-2 | | £ | 20-2 | | £ |
| | | | 31 May Purchases Day Book | PDB55 | 3,001.20 |

| Dr | | Purchases Account (GL5100) | | Cr |
|---|---|---|---|---|
| 20-2 | | £ | 20-2 | £ |
| 31 May Purchases Day Book | PDB55 | 2,501.00 | | |

## PURCHASES LEDGER

| Dr | | S Burston (PL530) | | Cr |
|---|---|---|---|---|
| 20-2 | | £ | 20-2 | £ |
| | | | 9 May Purchases | PDB55 318.00 |
| | | | 23 May Purchases | PDB55 512.40 |

| Dr | | Iley Supplies Limited (PL605) | | Cr |
|---|---|---|---|---|
| 20-2 | | £ | 20-2 | £ |
| | | | 12 May Purchases | PDB55 540.00 |

| Dr | | Malvern Manufacturing (PL625) | | Cr |
|---|---|---|---|---|
| 20-2 | | £ | 20-2 | £ |
| | | | 3 May Purchases | PDB55 204.00 |
| | | | 30 May Purchases | PDB55 436.80 |

| Dr | | SG Enterprises (PL720) | | Cr |
|---|---|---|---|---|
| 20-2 | | £ | 20-2 | £ |
| | | | 18 May Purchases | PDB55 990.00 |

**7.5**    **(a)**

| Purchases Returns Day Book | | | | | | PRDB14 |
|---|---|---|---|---|---|---|
| Date | Details | Credit note number | Account code | Total | VAT | Net |
| 20-2 | | | | £ | £ | £ |
| 11 May | Malvern Manufacturing | CN345 | PL625 | 84.00 | 14.00 | 70.00 |
| 17 May | Iley Supplies Ltd | CN241 | PL605 | 102.00 | 17.00 | 85.00 |
| 24 May | SG Enterprises | 85 | PL720 | 30.00 | 5.00 | 25.00 |
| 31 May | S Burston | SB95 | PL530 | 66.00 | 11.00 | 55.00 |
| 31 May | Totals for month | | | 282.00 | 47.00 | 235.00 |
| | | | | GL2350 | GL2200 | GL5110 |

**(b)**                                                    **GENERAL LEDGER**

Dr                          **Value Added Tax Account** (GL2200)                          Cr

| 20-2 | | | £ | 20-2 | | | £ |
|---|---|---|---|---|---|---|---|
| 31 May | Purchases Day Book | PDB55 | 500.20 | 31 May | Purchases Returns Day Book | PRDB14 | 47.00 |

Dr                    **Purchases Ledger Control Account** (GL2350)                    Cr

| 20-2 | | | £ | 20-2 | | | £ |
|---|---|---|---|---|---|---|---|
| 31 May | Purchases Returns Day Book | PRDB14 | 282.00 | 31 May | Purchases Day Book | PDB55 | 3,001.20 |

Dr                        **Purchases Returns Account** (GL5110)                        Cr

| 20-2 | | | £ | 20-2 | | | £ |
|---|---|---|---|---|---|---|---|
| | | | | 31 May | Purchases Returns Day Book | PRDB14 | 235.00 |

**PURCHASES LEDGER**

Dr                                **S Burston** (PL530)                                Cr

| 20-2 | | | £ | 20-2 | | | £ |
|---|---|---|---|---|---|---|---|
| 31 May | Purchases Returns | PRDB14 | 66.00 | 9 May | Purchases | PDB55 | 318.00 |
| | | | | 23 May | Purchases | PDB55 | 512.40 |

| Dr | | | Iley Supplies Limited (PL605) | | | Cr |
|---|---|---|---|---|---|---|
| 20-2 | | £ | 20-2 | | | £ |
| 17 May | Purchases Returns | | 12 May | Purchases | PDB55 | 540.00 |
| | PRDB14 | 102.00 | | | | |

| Dr | | | Malvern Manufacturing (PL625) | | | Cr |
|---|---|---|---|---|---|---|
| 20-2 | | £ | 20-2 | | | £ |
| 11 May | Purchases Returns | | 3 May | Purchases | PDB55 | 204.00 |
| | PRDB14 | 84.00 | 30 May | Purchases | PDB55 | 436.80 |

| Dr | | | SG Enterprises (PL720) | | | Cr |
|---|---|---|---|---|---|---|
| 20-2 | | £ | 20-2 | | | £ |
| 24 May | Purchases Returns | | 18 May | Purchases | PDB55 | 990.00 |
| | PRDB14 | 30.00 | | | | |

## 7.6 Purchases day book

| Date 20-4 | Details | Invoice number | Total £ | VAT £ | Net £ | Purchases type 1 £ | Purchases type 2 £ |
|---|---|---|---|---|---|---|---|
| 30 June | King & Co | K641 | 2,016 | 336 | 1,680 | | 1,680 |
| 30 June | Rossingtons | 2129 | 3,072 | 512 | 2,560 | 2,560 | |
| 30 June | Moniz Ltd | M/149 | 2,208 | 368 | 1,840 | | 1,840 |
| | Totals | | 7,296 | 1,216 | 6,080 | 2,560 | 3,520 |

**7.7** **(a)**

**Purchases ledger**

| Account name | Amount £ | Debit | Credit |
|---|---|---|---|
| H & L Ltd | 6,528 | | ✔ |
| Sperrin & Co | 2,208 | | ✔ |
| Hickmores | 4,608 | | ✔ |
| Marklew plc | 1,104 | | ✔ |

**General ledger**

| Account name | Amount £ | Debit | Credit |
|---|---|---|---|
| Purchases | 12,040 | ✔ | |
| Value Added Tax | 2,408 | ✔ | |
| Purchases ledger control | 14,448 | | ✔ |

**(b)**

**Purchases ledger**

| Account name | Amount £ | Debit | Credit |
|---|---|---|---|
| Marcer Transport | 624 | ✔ | |
| Schuller Ltd | 432 | ✔ | |

**General ledger**

| Account name | Amount £ | Debit | Credit |
|---|---|---|---|
| Purchases returns | 880 | | ✔ |
| Value Added Tax | 176 | | ✔ |
| Purchases ledger control | 1,056 | ✔ | |

**7.8**

**Purchases day book**

| Date 20-4 | Details | Invoice number | Total £ | VAT £ | Net £ | Product S12 £ | Product T12 £ |
|---|---|---|---|---|---|---|---|
| 30 June | Lyster Ltd | 4681 | 1,200.00 | 200.00 | 1000.00 | 1,000.00 | |
| 30 June | T England | 6234 | 432.00 | 72.00 | 360.00 | | 360.00 |
| 30 June | Mere Ltd | 1634 | 1,080.00 | 180.00 | 900.00 | | 900.00 |
| 30 June | J Mehta | 8561 | 480.00 | 80.00 | 400.00 | 400.00 | |
| | **Totals** | | 3,192.00 | 532.00 | 2,660.00 | 1,400.00 | 1,260.00 |

# 8 Prepare payments to suppliers

**8.1** An increase in the total amount owing shown on the statement of account

**8.2** Purchase invoices, purchase credit notes, total amount owing

**8.3** Will reduce the total amount shown as owing on the statement of account

**8.4** **(a)** Cheque for £1,000

**(b)** Invoice 790

**(c)** £360

**8.5** **(a)** The BACS remittance advice will be sent without a cheque to A Strauss & Co

**(b)** 30 April

**(c)** Invoice 2461, invoice 2479, credit note CN105

**(d)** £3,640

# 9 Three column cash book

**9.1** The debit side of discount allowed account

**9.2** **(a)** **Sales ledger**

| Account name | Amount £ | Debit | Credit |
|---|---|---|---|
| Boscawen Ltd | 1,540 | | ✔ |
| Boscawen Ltd | 45 | | ✔ |

**(b)** **General ledger**

| Account name | Amount £ | Debit | Credit |
|---|---|---|---|
| Discounts allowed | 45 | ✔ | |
| Sales ledger control | 1,540 | | ✔ |
| Sales ledger control | 45 | | ✔ |

**(c)** **General ledger**

| Account name | Amount £ | Debit | Credit |
|---|---|---|---|
| Wages | 1,265 | ✔ | |
| Office equipment | 1,968 | ✔ | |

**9.3** **(a)** **Sales ledger**

| Account name | Amount £ | Debit | Credit |
|---|---|---|---|
| Smithsons Ltd | 2,750 | | ✔ |
| Smithsons Ltd | 100 | | ✔ |

**(b)** **General ledger**

| Account name | Amount £ | Debit | Credit |
|---|---|---|---|
| Discounts allowed | 100 | ✔ | |
| Sales ledger control | 2,750 | | ✔ |
| Sales ledger control | 100 | | ✔ |
| Wages | 1,175 | ✔ | |
| Rent | 1,200 | ✔ | |
| Stationery | 120 | ✔ | |

**9.4** **(a)** True

**(b)** False – the balance b/d of £201 on 1 October shows that, according to the cash book, there is a bank overdraft.

**(c)** **GENERAL LEDGER**

| Dr | | **Sales Account** | | Cr |
|---|---|---|---|---|
| 20-1 | | £ | 20-1 | £ |
| | | | 30 Sep   Bank          CB68 | 88 |

| Dr | | **Sales Ledger Control Account** | | Cr |
|---|---|---|---|---|
| 20-1 | | £ | 20-1 | £ |
| | | | 30 Sep   Bank              CB68 | 1,580 |
| | | | 30 Sep   Discount allowed  CB68 | 25 |

| Dr | | **Purchases Ledger Control Account** | | Cr |
|---|---|---|---|---|
| 20-1 | | £ | 20-1 | £ |
| 30 Sep   Bank              CB68 | 1,940 | | | |
| 30 Sep   Discount received  CB68 | 30 | | | |

| Dr | | **Purchases Account** | | Cr |
|---|---|---|---|---|
| 20-1 | | £ | 20-1 | £ |
| 30 Sep   Bank          CB68 | 192 | | | |

| Dr | | **General Expenses Account** | | Cr |
|---|---|---|---|---|
| 20-1 | | £ | 20-1 | £ |
| 30 Sep   Bank          CB68 | 128 | | | |

| Dr | | **Wages Account** | | Cr |
|---|---|---|---|---|
| 20-1 | | £ | 20-1 | £ |
| 30 Sep   Bank          CB68 | 1,254 | | | |

| Dr | | **Office Equipment Account** | | Cr |
|---|---|---|---|---|
| 20-1 | | £ | 20-1 | £ |
| 30 Sep   Bank          CB68 | 1,440 | | | |

| Dr | | **Discount Allowed Account** | | Cr |
|---|---|---|---|---|
| 20-1 | | £ | 20-1 | £ |
| 30 Sep   Sales ledger        CB68 | 25 | | | |
| control | | | | |

| Dr | | | **Discount Received Account** | | | Cr |
|---|---|---|---|---|---|---|
| 20-1 | | | £ | 20-1 | | £ |
| | | | | 30 Sep | Purchases ledger control  CB68 | 30 |

**(d)**

**SALES LEDGER**

| Dr | | | **Albany Limited** | | | Cr |
|---|---|---|---|---|---|---|
| 20-1 | | | £ | 20-1 | | £ |
| | | | | 30 Sep | Bank  CB68 | 1,580 |
| | | | | 30 Sep | Discount allowed  CB68 | 25 |

**PURCHASES LEDGER**

| Dr | | | **Nelson Stores** | | Cr |
|---|---|---|---|---|---|
| 20-1 | | | £ | 20-1 | £ |
| 30 Sep | Bank | CB68 | 1,940 | | |
| 30 Sep | Discount received | CB68 | 30 | | |

**9.5**

**Cash Book**

Dr | | | | | | Cr

| Date 20-7 | Details | Discount £ | Cash £ | Bank £ | Date 20-7 | Details | Discount £ | Cash £ | Bank £ |
|---|---|---|---|---|---|---|---|---|---|
| 3 Aug | Balance b/d | | 286 | | 3 Aug | Balance b/d | | | 3,472 |
| 4 Aug | Sales | | 334 | | 3 Aug | Rent | | | 760 |
| 5 Aug | Murphy Ltd | 15 | | 1,475 | 8 Aug | Rates | | | 223 |
| | | | | | 8 Aug | JJ Supplies | 10 | | 490 |
| 10 Aug | Balance c/d | | | 3,870 | 10 Aug | Drawings | | | 400 |
| | | | | | 10 Aug | Wages | | 480 | |
| | | | | | 10 Aug | Balance c/d | | 140 | |
| | | 15 | 620 | 5,345 | | | 10 | 620 | 5,345 |
| 11 Aug | Balance b/d | | 140 | | 11 Aug | Balance b/d | | | 3,870 |
| | | | | | | | | | |
| | | | | | | | | | |

**9.6**

| Dr | | | | | Emma Maxwell Cash Book | | | | | Cr |
|---|---|---|---|---|---|---|---|---|---|---|
| **Date** **20-3** | **Details** | **Discount** £ | **Cash** £ | **Bank** £ | **Date** **20-3** | **Details** | **Discount** £ | **Cash** £ | **Bank** £ |
| 1 Mar | Balance b/d | | 200 | | 1 Mar | Balance b/d | | | 1,898 |
| 6 Mar | Court Ltd | | | 1,236 | 2 Mar | Lindum Supplies | 6 | | 254 |
| 13 Mar | H Sweeney        BACS | 10 | | 1,696 | 11 Mar | Rent | | | 550 |
| 14 Mar | Sales | | 639 | | 23 Mar | Wages | | 655 | |
| 24 Mar | Sales | | 786 | | 26 Mar | Wyvern Council        SO | | | 195 |
| 28 Mar | Mills & Co Ltd     BACS | | | 477 | 27 Mar | Bank interest | | | 45 |
| | | | | | 31 Mar | Balances c/d | | 970 | 467 |
| | | 10 | 1,625 | 3,409 | | | 6 | 1,625 | 3,409 |
| 1 Apr | Balances b/d | | 970 | 467 | | | | | |

| Dr | | | Discount Allowed Account | | Cr |
|---|---|---|---|---|---|
| **Date** **20-3** | **Details** | **£** | **Date** **20-3** | **Details** | **£** |
| 31 Mar | Sales ledger control | 10 | | | |

| Dr | | | Discount Received Account | | Cr |
|---|---|---|---|---|---|
| **Date** **20-3** | **Details** | **£** | **Date** **20-3** | **Details** | **£** |
| | | | 31 Mar | Purchases ledger control | 6 |

# 10 Analysed cash book

**10.1** BACS transfer from a trade receivable for £1,950

**10.2** Debit card payment to a trade payable for £940

**10.3**

| | Statement | True | False |
|---|---|---|---|
| **(a)** | Cash and bank control accounts are the general ledger accounts when cash book is used as a book of prime entry only | ✔ | |
| **(b)** | The purchases ledger column total from cash book is credited to purchases ledger control account in general ledger | | ✔ |
| **(c)** | The discount allowed column total from cash book is credited to discount allowed account in general ledger | | ✔ |
| **(d)** | The VAT column total on the payments side of cash book is debited to VAT account in general ledger | ✔ | |

**10.4** **(a)** **Cash book – credit side**

| Details | Discount £ | Cash £ | Bank £ | VAT £ | Trade payables £ | Cash purchases £ | Stationery expenses £ |
|---|---|---|---|---|---|---|---|
| Balance b/f | | | | | | | |
| Clark & Co | | 48 | | 8 | | 40 | |
| T Kinnear | | 192 | | 32 | | 160 | |
| Gaskin Ltd | 15 | | 1,690 | | 1,690 | | |
| Bristow Stationery | | | 144 | 24 | | | 120 |
| Roussouw & Co | | | 1,140 | | 1,140 | | |
| **Totals** | 15 | 240 | 2,974 | 64 | 2,830 | 200 | 120 |

**(b)** **Cash book – debit side**

| Details | Discount £ | Cash £ | Bank £ | Trade receivables £ |
|---|---|---|---|---|
| Balance b/f | | 642 | 1,022 | |
| Passmores | | | 455 | 455 |
| S McNulty | 15 | | 833 | 833 |
| **Totals** | 15 | 642 | 2,310 | 1,288 |

**(c)** | £402 |

**(d)** | £664 |

**(e)**

| Debit | |
|---|---|
| Credit | ✔ |

**10.5** **(a)**

**Cash book – credit side**

| Details | Discount £ | Cash £ | Bank £ | VAT £ | Trade payables £ | Cash purchases £ | Other expenses £ |
|---|---|---|---|---|---|---|---|
| Balance b/f | | | 2,417 | | | | |
| Mary Wallbank | | 192 | | 32 | | 160 | |
| Wenton Council | | | 425 | | | | 425 |
| Sanders plc | 10 | | 588 | | 588 | | |
| J Panas | | | 672 | | 672 | | |
| **Totals** | 10 | 192 | 4,102 | 32 | 1,260 | 160 | 425 |

**(b)**

**Cash book – debit side**

| Details | Discount £ | Cash £ | Bank £ | Trade receivables £ | Other income £ |
|---|---|---|---|---|---|
| Balance b/f | | 208 | | | |
| LFJ plc | | | 1,685 | 1,685 | |
| Wragg Ltd | 20 | | 2,135 | 2,135 | |
| Nikki Shah | | 200 | | | 200 |
| **Totals** | 20 | 408 | 3,820 | 3,820 | 200 |

**(c)**  £216

**(d)**  £–282

**(e)**

| Account name | Amount | Debit | Credit |
|---|---|---|---|
| Sanders plc | 10 | ✔ | |

# 11 Petty cash book

**11.1**   The petty cash float is restored to the same amount for the beginning of each week or month

**11.2**   Debit petty cash control £108; credit bank £108

**11.3**

| Statement | True | False |
|---|---|---|
| Payments are recorded on the debit side of petty cash book | | ✔ |
| A petty cash book may combine the roles of a book of prime entry and double-entry bookkeeping | ✔ | |
| Petty cash vouchers are authorised for payments by the petty cashier | | ✔ |
| The totals of the petty cash analysis columns are transferred to general ledger where they are debited to the appropriate expense account | ✔ | |

**11.4**   £139.90

**11.5**   £72.77

## 11.6    General ledger

| Account name | Amount £ | Debit | Credit |
|---|---|---|---|
| Petty cash book | 110 | ✔ | |
| Bank | 110 | | ✔ |

## 11.7    General ledger

| Account name | Amount £ | Debit | Credit |
|---|---|---|---|
| VAT | 5.60 | ✔ | |
| Postage | 11.50 | ✔ | |
| Travel expenses | 34.75 | ✔ | |
| Stationery | 15.60 | ✔ | |
| Bank | 57.00 | | ✔ |

**11.8 (a)**

**GENERAL LEDGER**

Dr | | | | Value Added Tax Account | | | Cr
---|---|---|---|---|---|---|---
20-6 | | | £ | 20-6 | | | £
31 Jul | Petty cash book | PCB35 | 4.32 | | | |

Dr | | | | Travel Account | | | Cr
---|---|---|---|---|---|---|---
20-6 | | | £ | 20-6 | | | £
31 Jul | Petty cash book | PCB35 | 26.00 | | | |

Dr | | | | Postages Account | | | Cr
---|---|---|---|---|---|---|---
20-6 | | | £ | 20-6 | | | £
31 Jul | Petty cash book | PCB35 | 11.55 | 14 Jul | Petty cash book | PCB35 | 6.25

Dr | | | | Stationery Account | | | Cr
---|---|---|---|---|---|---|---
20-6 | | | £ | 20-6 | | | £
31 Jul | Petty cash book | PCB35 | 13.20 | | | |

Dr | | | | Meals Account | | | Cr
---|---|---|---|---|---|---|---
20-6 | | | £ | 20-6 | | | £
31 Jul | Petty cash book | PCB35 | 10.00 | | | |

Dr | | | | Purchases Ledger Control Account | | | Cr
---|---|---|---|---|---|---|---
20-6 | | | £ | 20-6 | | | £
31 Jul | Petty cash book | PCB35 | 18.25 | | | |

Dr | | | | Petty Cash Control Account | | | Cr
---|---|---|---|---|---|---|---
20-6 | | | £ | 20-6 | | | £
1 Jul | Balance b/d | | 200.00 | 31 Jul | Petty cash book | PCB35 | 83.32
31 Jul | Petty cash book | PCB35 | 6.25 | 31 Jul | Balance c/d | | 200.00
31 Jul | Bank | CB | 77.07 | | | |
 | | | 283.32 | | | | 283.32
1 Aug | Balance b/d | | 200.00 | | | |

Dr | | | | Cash Book | | | Cr
---|---|---|---|---|---|---|---
20-6 | | | Bank | 20-6 | | | Bank
 | | | | 31 Jul | Petty cash | PCB35 | 77.07

**(b)**

**PURCHASES LEDGER**

Dr | | | | J Clarke | | | Cr
---|---|---|---|---|---|---|---
20-6 | | | £ | 20-6 | | | £
22 Jul | Petty cash book | PCB35 | 18.25 | | | |

**11.9 (a) and (b)**

**Petty cash book**

| Debit side | | Credit side | | | | | |
|---|---|---|---|---|---|---|---|
| Details | Amount £ | Details | Amount £ | VAT £ | Postage £ | Travel £ | Repairs £ |
| Balance b/f | 150.00 | Post office | 10.70 | | 10.70 | | |
| | | City Taxis | 14.40 | 2.40 | | 12.00 | |
| | | Repair Shop Ltd | 22.56 | 3.76 | | | 18.80 |
| | | Balance c/d | 102.34 | | | | |
| | 150.00 | | 150.00 | 6.16 | 10.70 | 12.00 | 18.80 |

**11.10 (a)**

| | |
|---|---|
| Amount in petty cash box | £92.35 |
| Balance on petty cash account | £93.30 |
| Difference | £ 0.95 |

**(b)**

| | |
|---|---|
| Petty cash reimbursement | |
| Date: 30.04.20-5 | |
| Amount required to restore the cash in the petty cash box | £129.35 |

# 12 The initial trial balance

**12.1** Sales account

**12.2** Sales ledger control account

**12.3** **Trial balance of Kate Trelawney as at 31 March 20-2**

| Name of account | Dr £ | Cr £ |
|---|---|---|
| Bank loan | | 3,650 |
| Purchases | 23,745 | |
| Vehicle | 9,500 | |
| Sales | | 65,034 |
| Bank (cash at bank) | 2,162 | |
| Discount allowed | 317 | |
| Purchases returns | | 855 |
| Sales ledger control | 7,045 | |
| Office equipment | 5,450 | |
| Inventory at 1 April 20-1 | 4,381 | |
| Sales returns | 1,624 | |
| Purchases ledger control | | 4,736 |
| Expenses | 32,598 | |
| Discount received | | 494 |
| Capital *(missing figure)* | | 12,053 |
| | 86,822 | 86,822 |

**12.4**

| Account name | Amount £ | Debit £ | Credit £ |
|---|---|---|---|
| Bank (overdraft) | 4,293 | | 4,293 |
| Loan from bank | 12,500 | | 12,500 |
| Vehicles | 25,500 | 25,500 | |
| Inventory | 10,417 | 10,417 | |
| Petty cash control | 68 | 68 | |
| Capital | 25,794 | | 25,794 |
| VAT owing to HM Revenue & Customs | 1,496 | | 1,496 |
| Purchases ledger control | 12,794 | | 12,794 |
| Purchases | 104,763 | 104,763 | |
| Purchases returns | 2,681 | | 2,681 |
| Sales ledger control | 28,354 | 28,354 | |
| Sales | 184,267 | | 184,267 |
| Sales returns | 4,098 | 4,098 | |
| Discount allowed | 1,312 | 1,312 | |
| Discount received | 1,784 | | 1,784 |
| Wages | 35,961 | 35,961 | |
| Telephone | 3,474 | 3,474 | |
| Advertising | 5,921 | 5,921 | |
| Insurance | 3,084 | 3,084 | |
| Heating and lighting | 2,477 | 2,477 | |
| Rent and rates | 3,672 | 3,672 | |
| Postages | 876 | 876 | |
| Miscellaneous expenses | 545 | 545 | |
| Drawings | 15,087 | 15,087 | |
| Totals | – | 245,609 | 245,609 |

**12.5**

| Account name | Amount £ | Debit £ | Credit £ |
|---|---|---|---|
| Sales | 262,394 | | 262,394 |
| Sales returns | 2,107 | 2,107 | |
| Sales ledger control | 33,844 | 33,844 | |
| Purchases | 157,988 | 157,988 | |
| Purchases returns | 1,745 | | 1,745 |
| Purchases ledger control | 17,311 | | 17,311 |
| Discount received | 1,297 | | 1,297 |
| Discount allowed | 845 | 845 | |
| Rent and rates | 5,941 | 5,941 | |
| Advertising | 6,088 | 6,088 | |
| Insurance | 3,176 | 3,176 | |
| Wages | 48,954 | 48,954 | |
| Heating and lighting | 4,266 | 4,266 | |
| Postages and telephone | 2,107 | 2,107 | |
| Miscellaneous expenses | 632 | 632 | |
| Vehicles | 28,400 | 28,400 | |
| Capital | 48,756 | | 48,756 |
| Drawings | 19,354 | 19,354 | |
| Office equipment | 10,500 | 10,500 | |
| Inventory | 16,246 | 16,246 | |
| Petty cash control | 150 | 150 | |
| Bank (cash at bank) | 3,096 | 3,096 | |
| VAT owing to HM Revenue & Customs | 3,721 | | 3,721 |
| Loan from bank | 8,470 | | 8,470 |
| Totals | – | 343,694 | 343,694 |

**12.6**

| Item | Capital expenditure | Revenue expenditure | Capital income | Revenue income |
|---|---|---|---|---|
| Purchase of vehicles | ✔ | | | |
| Fuel for vehicles | | ✔ | | |
| Discounts received | | | | ✔ |
| Receipts from sale of office equipment | | | ✔ | |
| Redecoration of property | | ✔ | | |
| Extension to property | ✔ | | | |
| Receipts from sale of goods to credit customers | | | | ✔ |
| Delivery cost of new machine | ✔ | | | |
| Increase in owner's capital | | | ✔ | |
| Repairs to vehicles | | ✔ | | |

# Practice
# assessment 1

Complete all 10 tasks.

Each task is independent.  You will not need to refer to your answers in previous tasks.

The tasks are set in a business, Kington Supplies.

- You are employed by Kington Supplies, as a bookkeeper.

- Kington Supplies uses a manual bookkeeping system.

- Double-entry takes place in the general ledger. Individual accounts of trade receivables and trade payables are kept in the sales and purchases ledgers as subsidiary accounts.

- The cash book and petty cash book should be treated as part of the  double-entry system unless the task instructions state otherwise.

- The VAT rate is 20%.

**Task 1**

Purchase invoices and purchase credit notes have been received and partially entered in the day books, as shown below.

Complete the entries in the purchases day book and the purchases returns day book by:

- inserting the correct supplier account codes from the coding list below

- inserting the appropriate figures to complete the entries

| Coding list | |
|---|---|
| G Aveton | AVE001 |
| D Thurlestone | THU002 |
| Frogmore & Co | FRO001 |
| Halwell Ltd | HAL001 |
| Loddiwell Bros | LOD001 |
| Malborough Partners | MAL003 |
| Modbury Ltd | MOD001 |
| A P Morleigh | MOR002 |
| Torcross plc | TOR001 |

### Purchases day book

| Date 20-4 | Details | Supplier Account Code | Invoice number | Total £ | VAT £ | Net £ | Purchases A £ | Purchases B £ |
|---|---|---|---|---|---|---|---|---|
| 30 Jun | A P Morleigh | | CRO846 | 336 | | 280 | | 280 |
| 30 Jun | Loddiwell Bros | | 1532 | | 484 | | 420 | 2,000 |
| 30 Jun | Modbury Ltd | | 4591 | 1,296 | | | 1,080 | |

### Purchases returns day book

| Date 20-4 | Details | Supplier Account Code | Credit note number | Total £ | VAT £ | Net £ | Purchases A £ | Purchases B £ |
|---|---|---|---|---|---|---|---|---|
| 30 Jun | Torcross plc | | 7511 | 840 | | | 700 | |
| 30 Jun | Malborough Partners | | 10697 | | 28 | | 30 | 110 |

## Task 2

The following credit transactions have been entered into the sales returns day book as shown below. No entries have yet been made into the ledgers.

### Sales returns day book

| Date 20-4 | Details | Credit note number | Total £ | VAT £ | Net £ |
|---|---|---|---|---|---|
| 30 Jun | Avon & Co | CN36 | 288 | 48 | 240 |
| 30 Jun | Portlemouth Ltd | CN37 | 744 | 124 | 620 |
| | | Totals | 1,032 | 172 | 860 |

**(a)**

What will be the entries in the subsidiary sales ledger?

Select the account names from the following list: Avon & Co, Portlemouth Ltd, Purchases, Purchases ledger control, Purchases returns, Sales, Sales ledger control, Sales returns, VAT.

Enter the names and amounts and tick the appropriate debit or credit column.

**Sales ledger**

| Account name | Amount £ | Debit ✔ | Credit ✔ |
|---|---|---|---|
|  |  |  |  |
|  |  |  |  |

**(b)**

What will be the entries in the general ledger?

Select your account name from the following list: Avon & Co, Portlemouth Ltd, Purchases, Purchases ledger control, Purchases returns, Sales, Sales ledger control, Sales returns, VAT.

Enter the names and amounts and tick the appropriate debit or credit column.

**General ledger**

| Account name | Amount £ | Debit ✔ | Credit ✔ |
|---|---|---|---|
|  |  |  |  |
|  |  |  |  |
|  |  |  |  |

## Task 3

There are three payments to be entered in the credit side of Kington Supplies' cash book during one week.

**Cash purchases listing**

| Suppliers paid in cash | Net £ | VAT £ | Gross £ |
|---|---|---|---|
| Alvington Supplies | 150 | 30 | 180 |

**Trade payables listing**

| Credit suppliers paid by cheque | Amount paid £ | Discount taken £ |
|---|---|---|
| Halwell Ltd | 2,106 | 45 |
| Frogmore & Co | 1,164 | 30 |

**(a)**

From the cash purchases listing and the trade payables listing above, make entries in the relevant columns of the credit side of the cash book shown below.

Select your entries for the Details column from the following list: Alvington Supplies, Bank, Cash, Cash purchases, Discount, Halwell Ltd, Trade payables, Frogmore & Co, VAT.

**(b)**

Total each column.

**Cash book – credit side**

| Details | Discount £ | Cash £ | Bank £ | VAT £ | Trade payables £ | Cash purchases £ |
|---|---|---|---|---|---|---|
| Balance b/f | | | 4,720 | | | |
| | | | | | | |
| | | | | | | |
| | | | | | | |
| Totals | | | | | | |

**(c)**

The debit side of the cash book shows the cash balance brought forward at the beginning of the week was £250 and a further £412 has been received during the week.

Using your answers above, calculate the cash balance.

£ [                    ]

**(d)**

The debit side of the cash book shows the total amount of money banked during the week was £5,341.

Using your answers above, calculate the bank balance.  If your calculations show that the bank account is overdrawn, your answer should start with a minus sign, for example –123.

£ [                    ]

**Task 4**

Kington Supplies' cash book is both a book of prime entry and part of the double-entry bookkeeping system. These are the totals of the columns in the credit side of the cash book at the end of the month.

**Cash book - credit side**

| Details | Discount | Cash | Bank | VAT | Trade payables | Cash purchases | Bank charges |
|---------|----------|------|------|-----|----------------|----------------|--------------|
|         | £ | £ | £ | £ | £ | £ | £ |
| Totals  | 159 | 648 | 15,980 | 108 | 15,928 | 540 | 52 |

**(a)**
What will be the **SIX** entries in the general ledger?

Select your account name from the following list:  Bank, Bank charges, Cash, Cash purchases, Cash sales, Discount taken, Discount given, Purchases ledger control, Sales ledger control, Trade payables, VAT.

Enter the names and amounts and tick the appropriate debit or credit column.

**General ledger**

| Account name | Amount £ | Debit ✔ | Credit ✔ |
|---|---|---|---|
|  |  |  |  |
|  |  |  |  |
|  |  |  |  |
|  |  |  |  |
|  |  |  |  |
|  |  |  |  |

**(b)**

One of the bank payments to trade payables was to H King for £254.

What will be the entry in the purchases ledger?

Select your account name from the following list: Bank, Kington Supplies, H King, Purchases, Purchases ledger, Purchases ledger control, Sales, Sales ledger, Sales ledger control, Trade payables.

Enter the names and amounts and tick the appropriate debit or credit column.

**Purchases ledger**

| Account name | Amount £ | Debit ✔ | Credit ✔ |
|---|---|---|---|
|  |  |  |  |

**Task 5**

Kington Supplies maintains a petty cash book as a book of prime entry and part of the double-entry bookkeeping system.  This is a summary of petty cash purchases during the week.

- •   A4 paper £20 plus VAT
- •   Window cleaning £10. VAT not applicable

**(a)**

Enter the above transactions into the partially completed petty cash book below.

Select your entry for the Details column from the following list: Balance c/d, Balance b/f, Cleaning, Paper, Office expenses, VAT.

**(b)**

Total the petty cash book and show the balance carried down.

**Petty cash book**

| Details | Amount £ | Details | Amount £ | VAT £ | Office expenses £ | Cleaning £ |
|---|---|---|---|---|---|---|
| Balance b/f | 100.00 | Postage | 40.00 | | 40.00 | |
| | | | | | | |
| | | | | | | |
| | | | | | | |
| Total | 100.00 | Totals | | | | |

**(c)**

What will be the **THREE** accounts in the general ledger which will record the above transactions?

Tick the appropriate accounts in the right-hand column.

                             ✔

| | |
|---|---|
| Office expenses | |
| Petty cash control | |
| Postage | |
| Telephone | |
| VAT | |
| Petty cash book | |
| Cleaning | |

**(d)**

The notes and coins that are now in the petty cash box are as follows:

| |
|---|
| 1 x £10 note |
| 2 x £5 notes |
| 4 x £1 coins |
| 3 x 50p coins |
| 1 x 20p coin |
| 2 x 10p coins |
| 2 x 5p coins |

Does the amount of cash in the petty cash box reconcile with the balance in the petty cash book?

Tick the correct option.

✔

Yes, the amount of cash in the petty cash box reconciles with the balance in the petty cash book

No, there is not enough cash in the petty cash box

No, there is too much cash in the petty cash box

**(e)**

At the end of the week what is the amount of cash that would have to be withdrawn from the bank to restore the imprest level of £100?

£

**(f)**

Each petty cash claim is processed using a petty cash voucher.

Select **TWO** details that you would **not** expect to see on the petty cash voucher.

Tick the correct options.

| | ✔ |
|---|---|
| Amount of cash being claimed | |
| Signature of claimant | |
| Any VAT applicable | |
| Amount of imprest level | |
| Date | |
| Voucher number | |
| Details of item purchased | |
| Balance of cash in box | |
| Signature of person authorising the claim | |

**Task 6**

A list of balances to be transferred to the trial balance is shown below.

Place the figures in the debit or credit column, as appropriate, and total each column.

Do not enter figures with decimal places in this task.

**Trial balance as at 30 June**

| Account name | Amount | Debit | Credit |
|---|---|---|---|
| | £ | £ | £ |
| Sales | 104,693 | | |
| Sales ledger control | 14,446 | | |
| Sales returns | 5,279 | | |
| Purchases | 57,254 | | |
| Purchases ledger control | 8,516 | | |
| Purchases returns | 821 | | |
| Discount received (taken) | 881 | | |
| Discount allowed (given) | 702 | | |
| Rent and rates | 5,149 | | |
| Advertising | 4,385 | | |
| Insurance | 2,537 | | |
| Wages | 27,234 | | |
| Heating and lighting | 2,494 | | |
| Office expenses | 1,754 | | |
| Telephone | 1,976 | | |
| Cleaning | 823 | | |
| Capital | 22,262 | | |
| Office equipment | 19,680 | | |
| Inventory | 8,080 | | |
| Petty cash | 100 | | |
| Bank (money in bank) | 3,711 | | |
| VAT owing to HMRC | 3,284 | | |
| Loan from bank | 15,146 | | |
| Totals | – | | |

**Task 7**

This is a summary of Kington Supplies' transactions with their supplier D Thurlestone. D Thurlestone has agreed to allow Kington Supplies to make payments by the last day of the second month following the month of invoice. For example, invoices issued in January will be due for payment by 31 March.

| Date | Details | Amount £ |
|---|---|---|
| 2 April | Invoice 52974 | 1,200 |
| 19 April | Invoice 60821 | 960 |
| 29 April | Credit note 428 | 156 |
| 7 May | Invoice 62730 | 1,020 |
| 10 May | Credit note 455 | 960 |
| 12 May | Invoice 63000 | 840 |
| 31 May | Invoice 64411 | 600 |
| 15 June | Invoice 64962 | 1,440 |
| 25 June | Invoice 65007 | 720 |

**(a)**

Complete the table below by:

- inserting the total of transactions with D Thurlestone in each of the months: April, May, and June.

- showing the dates by which each payment should be made by entering the relevant date in the right-hand column.

Choose from: 30 April, 31 May, 30 June, 31 July, 31 August.

| Month | Amount £ | Payments to be made by |
|---|---|---|
| Transactions in April | | |
| Transactions in May | | |
| Transactions in June | | |

**(b)**

Kington Supplies has received a statement of account from D Thurlestone.

<table>
<tr><td colspan="4" align="center">**D Thurlestone**<br>22 Royal Garden Street<br>Plyminster, PL4 1NJ<br>STATEMENT OF ACCOUNT</td></tr>
<tr><td colspan="2">To: Kington Supplies</td><td colspan="2" align="right">Date: 30 June</td></tr>
<tr><td>**Date**</td><td>**Reference number**</td><td>**Details**</td><td>**Amount £**</td></tr>
<tr><td>2 April</td><td>52974</td><td>Goods</td><td>1,200</td></tr>
<tr><td>19 April</td><td>60821</td><td>Goods</td><td>960</td></tr>
<tr><td>7 May</td><td>62730</td><td>Goods</td><td>1,020</td></tr>
<tr><td>10 May</td><td>455</td><td>Goods returned</td><td>960</td></tr>
<tr><td>12 May</td><td>63000</td><td>Goods</td><td>840</td></tr>
<tr><td>31 May</td><td>64411</td><td>Goods</td><td>600</td></tr>
<tr><td>25 June</td><td>65007</td><td>Goods</td><td>720</td></tr>
<tr><td></td><td></td><td>Total outstanding</td><td>4,380</td></tr>
</table>

Using the data in (a) show what **TWO** items are missing from the statement of account by ticking the relevant items below.

| | ✔ |
|---|---|
| Invoice 52974 | |
| Invoice 60821 | |
| Credit note 428 | |
| Invoice 62730 | |
| Credit note 455 | |
| Invoice 63000 | |
| Invoice 64411 | |
| Invoice 64962 | |
| Invoice 65007 | |

**(c)**

On 15 July Kington Supplies received an invoice from D Thurlestone. The invoice is shown below together with the delivery note.

## D Thurlestone

22 Royal Garden Street

Plyminster, PL4 1NJ

VAT Registration No. 298 3881 04

| Kington Supplies<br>8 Beeching Road<br>Kington<br>KN7 1RR | Invoice no: 66068<br><br>Date: 15 July 20-4 | | | |
|---|---|---|---|---|
| **Quantity** | **Description** | **Unit price**<br>£ | **Total**<br>£ | **Net amount**<br>£ |
| 600 | Product A10011 | 1.50 | 900.00 | 900.00 |
| Terms:<br>3% discount for payment within 14 days | | | VAT | 180.00 |
| | | | Total | 1080.00 |

## D Thurlestone

22 Royal Garden Street

Plyminster, PL4 1NJ

VAT Registration No. 298 3881 04

| Kington Supplies<br>8 Beeching Road<br>Kington<br>KN7 1RR | Delivery note 100423<br><br>Date: 13 July 20-4 |
|---|---|
| Quantity | Description |
| 600 | Product A10011 |

Signed for by (signature) ...... *N. Hall* ............... Print name ........... N. Hall ....................................

Check the delivery note and the invoice and answer the following questions.

| Questions | Yes ✔ | No ✔ |
|---|---|---|
| Has the correct product been delivered? | | |
| Has the correct quantity been delivered? | | |
| Has the correct net price been calculated? | | |
| Has the settlement discount been applied? | | |

**(d)**

What will be the correct amounts on the invoice?

Enter the amounts below.

| Net amount £ | VAT amount £ | Gross amount £ |
|---|---|---|
| | | |

**Task 8**

**(a)**

Kington Supplies has received a cheque for £2,070 from a credit customer, Strete Ltd. No document was included with the cheque to show what transactions were included in the payment.

Show what document the customer should have included with the cheque by ticking against one of the following:

| | ✔ |
|---|---|
| Sales invoice | |
| Delivery note | |
| Sales order | |
| Remittance advice | |

**(b)**

This is the account of Strete Ltd in Kington Supplies' sales ledger.

| | Strete Ltd | | | Account code: STR002 | |
|---|---|---|---|---|---|
| **Date** | **Details** | **Amount £** | **Date** | **Details** | **Amount £** |
| 1 June | Balance b/d | 1,590 | 1 June | Bank | 1,416 |
| 5 June | Invoice 523 | 420 | 5 June | Cr note 72 | 174 |
| 18 June | Invoice 559 | 810 | | | |
| 22 June | Invoice 602 | 1,260 | | | |

Complete the following statement by ticking the correct word options set out below:

The cheque from Strete Ltd for £2,070 has resulted in an

| | ✔ |
|---|---|
| under-payment | |
| over-payment | |

This probably relates to

| | ✔ |
|---|---|
| balance b/d | |
| invoice 523 | |
| invoice 559 | |
| invoice 602 | |
| credit note 72 | |
| bank payment 1 June | |

In order to resolve the problem Kington Supplies should

| | ✔ |
|---|---|
| request a remittance advice | |
| request a credit note | |
| request further payment | |

from Strete Ltd for

| | ✔ |
|---|---|
| £810 | |
| £420 | |
| £174 | |

which will clear the outstanding balance.

**(c)**

On 14 July Kington Supplies received the following purchase order from Strete Ltd. The goods were delivered the following day. The customer has been offered a 10% trade discount and a 2% settlement discount for payment with 7 days.

---

## PURCHASE ORDER
**Strete Ltd**

**No** 908
**Date** 14 07 20-4

The Old Station, Torton, TR3 8TT

---

To: Kington Supplies

Please supply 250 units of product code B477

Purchase price: £5 each, plus VAT @ 20%.

Discount: less 10% trade discount, as agreed

---

Complete the **TEN** boxes in the sales invoice below.

---

# Kington Supplies
8 Beeching Road

Kington

KN7 1RR

| Date: 15 July 20-4 | | | | Sales invoice no. 66068 | |
| --- | --- | --- | --- | --- | --- |
| Customer account code: | | | | Purchase order no. | |

| Quantity | Product code | Price each £ | Total £ | Trade discount £ | Goods £ |
| --- | --- | --- | --- | --- | --- |
| | | | | | |

| | | | VAT | |
| --- | --- | --- | --- | --- |
| Terms: 2% settlement discount for payment within 7 days | | | Total | |

**Task 9**

The following account is in the sales ledger at the close of day on 30 June.

**(a)**

Insert the balance carried down together with date and details.

**(b)**

Insert the totals.

**(c)**

Insert the balance brought down together with the date and details.

| | | | | | |
|---|---|---|---|---|---|
| | | **E Beeson & Sons** | | | **BEE001** |
| Date | Details | Amount £ | Date | Details | Amount £ |
| 1 June | Balance b/d | 478 | 25 June | Bank | 406 |
| 29 June | Invoice 651 | 996 | 30 June | Credit note CN29 | 72 |
| | | | | | |
| | | | | | |

**(d)**

Complete the statement of account to be sent to E Beeson & Sons by:

- Entering transactions in the details column of the statement of account and choosing the correct options from the following: BACS £406, Credit note CN29 £72, Invoice 651 £996, Opening balance £478.

- Entering the amount outstanding after every transaction into the final column of the statement of account.

# Kington Supplies

8 Beeching Road

Kington

KN7 1RR

## STATEMENT OF ACCOUNT

| To: E Beeson & Sons | | Date: 30 June 20-4 |
|---|---|---|
| **Date** | **Details of individual transactions** | **Outstanding amount  £** |
| 1 June | | |
| 25 June | | |
| 29 June | | |
| 30 June | | |

**Task 10**

**(a)**

Kington Supplies started a new business, Kington Fabrications, on 1 July with the following assets and liabilities.

| Assets and liabilities | £ |
|---|---|
| Machinery | 17,500 |
| Bank loan | 15,000 |
| Inventory | 5,225 |
| Cash at bank | 2,275 |

Show the accounting equation on 1 July by calculating and inserting the appropriate figures.

| Assets | Liabilities | Capital |
|---|---|---|
| £ | £ | £ |
|  |  |  |

**(b)**

On 7 July the new business had the following assets and liabilities.

| Assets and liabilities | £ |
|---|---|
| Machinery | 17,500 |
| Bank loan | 15,000 |
| Inventory | 7,857 |
| Cash at bank | 3,548 |
| Trade receivables | 6,469 |
| Trade payables | 7,578 |

Show the accounting equation on 7 July by calculating and inserting the appropriate figures.

| Assets | Liabilities | Capital |
|---|---|---|
| £ | £ | £ |
|  |  |  |

**(c)**

Show whether the transactions of Kington Fabrications are classified as capital income, revenue income, capital expenditure or revenue expenditure by ticking the appropriate column.

| Item | Capital income ✔ | Revenue income ✔ | Capital expenditure ✔ | Revenue expenditure ✔ |
|---|---|---|---|---|
| Received cash for goods sold | | | | |
| Purchased new machinery | | | | |
| Paid rent on premises | | | | |
| Purchased goods for resale on credit | | | | |
| Received payment from a trade receivable | | | | |
| Received cash from owner | | | | |

**(d)**

The sales day book is part of the double-entry bookkeeping system. True or false?

Tick the correct option.

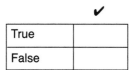

| | ✔ |
|---|---|
| True | |
| False | |

**(e)**

Kington Fabrications' credit customer accounts are given a unique customer code. The codes are made up of the first three letters of the customer's name, followed by the number of the ledger page allocated to each customer in that alphabetical group.

Kington Fabrications now has two new customers: Young & Co and Rogers Ltd.

Insert the relevant account code in the coding list below for each of the **TWO** new customers.

Select your choices from the following list: ROG001, YOU002, ROG002, YEL002, ROS002, YOU001.

| Customer name | Customer account code |
|---|---|
| GMG Gardens | GMG001 |
| Rogers Ltd | |
| Ross Welding Ltd | ROS001 |
| Southfield & Company | SOU002 |
| Swan Construction | SWA001 |
| Westend Builders | WES001 |
| Yellowstone Ltd | YEL001 |
| Young & Co | |

# Practice
# assessment 2

Complete all 10 tasks.

Each task is independent. You will not need to refer to your answers in previous tasks.

The tasks are set in a business where the following apply:

- You are employed by the business, GWW Trading, as a bookkeeper.

- GWW Trading uses a manual bookkeeping system.

- Double-entry takes place in the general ledger. Individual accounts of trade receivables and trade payables are kept in the sales and purchases ledgers as subsidiary accounts.

- The cash book and petty cash book should be treated as part of the double-entry system unless the task instructions state otherwise.

- The VAT rate is 20%.

## Task 1

Sales invoices and sales credit notes have been received and partially entered in the day books, as shown below.

Complete the entries in the sales day book and the sales returns day book by:

- selecting the correct customer account codes from the coding list below

- inserting the appropriate figures to complete the entries

| Coding list | |
|---|---|
| Ashley Supplies | ASHLEY |
| E Slattery Ltd | SLATTE |
| M Hamilton plc | HAMILT |
| O'Hara & Co | OHARA |
| R Butler Ltd | BUTLER |
| Scarlet Stores | SCARLE |
| Tarleton Bros | TARLET |
| Watling Enterprises | WATLIN |
| Wilkes & Son | WILKES |

**Sales day book**

| Date 20-4 | Details | Account code | Invoice number | Total £ | VAT £ | Net £ | Sales A £ | Sales B £ |
|---|---|---|---|---|---|---|---|---|
| 30 June | Tarleton Bros | | 1530 | | | 650 | 650 | |
| 30 June | E Slattery Ltd | | 1531 | | 164 | | | 820 |
| 30 June | Scarlet Stores | | 1532 | 2,088 | | | 760 | 980 |

**Sales returns day book**

| Date 20-4 | Details | Account code | Credit note number | Total £ | VAT £ | Net £ | Sales A £ | Sales B £ |
|---|---|---|---|---|---|---|---|---|
| 30 June | M Hamilton plc | | 140 | | 11 | | | 55 |
| 30 June | Wilkes & Son | | 141 | | | 195 | 195 | |

**Task 2**

The following credit transactions have been entered into the purchases returns day book as shown below.  No entries have yet been made into the ledgers.

**Purchases returns day book**

| Date 20-4 | Details | Credit note number | Total £ | VAT £ | Net £ |
|---|---|---|---|---|---|
| 30 June | India Trading | 1504 | 216 | 36 | 180 |
| 30 June | Kennedy Stores | CR99 | 150 | 25 | 125 |
| | | Totals | 366 | 61 | 305 |

**(a)**

What will be the entries in the subsidiary purchases ledger?

Select your account names from the following list: India Trading, Kennedy Stores, Purchases, Purchases ledger control, Purchases returns, Sales, Sales ledger control, Sales returns, VAT.

**Purchases ledger**

| Account name | Amount £ | Debit ✔ | Credit ✔ |
|---|---|---|---|
| | | | |
| | | | |

**(b)**

What will be the entries in the general ledger?

Select your account names from the following list: India Trading, Kennedy Stores, Purchases, Purchases ledger control, Purchases returns, Sales, Sales ledger control, Sales returns, VAT.

**General ledger**

| Account name | Amount £ | Debit ✔ | Credit ✔ |
|---|---|---|---|
| | | | |
| | | | |
| | | | |

**Task 3**

Three receipts are to be entered in the debit side of GWW Trading's cash book during one week.

**Cash sales listing**

| Customer receipts in cash | Net £ | VAT £ | Gross £ |
|---|---|---|---|
| Cash sales | 1,550 | 310 | 1860 |

**Trade receivables listing**

| Customer cheque receipts | Amount paid £ | Discount taken £ |
|---|---|---|
| Watling Enterprises | 1,240 | 50 |
| O'Hara & Co | 570 | 25 |

**(a)**

From the cash sales listing and the trade receivables listing above, make entries in the relevant columns of the debit side of the cash book shown on the next page.

Select your entries for the Details column from the following list: Bank, Cash, Cash sales, Discount, O'Hara & Co, Trade receivables, VAT, Watling Enterprises.

**(b)**

Total each column.

**Cash book – debit side**

| Details | Discount £ | Cash £ | Bank £ | VAT £ | Trade receivables £ | Cash sales £ |
|---------|------------|--------|--------|-------|---------------------|--------------|
| Balance b/f | | 156 | 2,369 | | | |
| | | | | | | |
| | | | | | | |
| | | | | | | |
| **Totals** | | | | | | |

**(c)**

The credit side of the cash book shows cash payments of £106 during the week.

Using your answers above, calculate the cash balance.

£ 

**(d)**

The credit side of the cash book shows the total bank payments during the week were £6,278.

Using your answers above, calculate the bank balance. If your calculations show that the bank account is overdrawn, your answer should start with a minus sign, for example –123.

£

## Task 4

GWW Trading's cash book is both a book of prime entry and part of the double-entry bookkeeping system. These are the totals of the columns in the debit side of the cash book at the end of the month.

**Cash book - debit side**

| Details | Discount £ | Cash £ | Bank £ | VAT £ | Trade receivables £ | Cash sales £ | Bank interest £ |
|---------|---------|------|------|-----|-----------------|------------|---------------|
| Totals | 275 | 8,568 | 6,640 | 1,428 | 6,613 | 7,140 | 27 |

**(a)**

What will be the **SIX** entries in the general ledger?

Select your account names from the following list: Bank, Bank interest received, Bank interest paid, Cash, Cash purchases, Cash sales, Discount given, Discount taken, Purchases ledger control, Sales ledger control, Trade receivables, VAT.

**General ledger**

| Account name | Amount £ | Debit ✔ | Credit ✔ |
|--------------|---------|--------|---------|
|  |  |  |  |
|  |  |  |  |
|  |  |  |  |
|  |  |  |  |
|  |  |  |  |
|  |  |  |  |

**(b)**

One of the bank receipts from trade receivables was from R Butler Ltd for £752.

What will be the entry in the sales ledger?

Select your account name from the following list:  Bank, R Butler Ltd, GWW Trading, Purchases, Purchases ledger, Purchases ledger control, Sales, Sales ledger, Sales ledger control, Trade receivables.

Enter the amounts and names and tick the appropriate debit or credit column.

| Account name | Amount £ | Debit ✔ | Credit ✔ |
|---|---|---|---|
|  |  |  |  |

## Task 5

GWW Trading maintains a petty cash book as a book of prime entry and part of the double-entry bookkeeping system. This is a summary of petty cash transactions in a week.

- Stamps £12.50. VAT not applicable
- Van repairs £58.80 including VAT

**(a)**

Enter the above transactions into the partially completed petty cash book below.

Select your entries for the Details column from the following list: Balance c/d, Balance b/f, Envelopes, Office expenses, Stamps, VAT, Van repairs, Vehicle expenses.

**(b)**

Total the petty cash book and show the balance carried down.

**Petty cash book**

| Details | Amount £ | Details | Amount £ | VAT £ | Office expenses £ | Vehicle expenses £ |
|---|---|---|---|---|---|---|
| Balance b/f | 100.00 | Envelopes | 6.72 | 1.12 | 5.60 |  |
|  |  | Balance c/d |  |  |  |  |
| Total | 100.00 | Totals |  |  |  |  |

**(c)**

What will be the **THREE** accounts in the general ledger which will record the above transactions?

✔

| | |
|---|---|
| Office expenses | |
| Petty cash control | |
| Stamps | |
| Van repairs | |
| VAT | |
| Petty cash book | |
| Vehicle expenses | |

These are the notes and coins that are now in the petty cash tin:

| |
|---|
| 1 x £10 note |
| 1 x £5 note |
| 6 x £1 coins |
| 1 x 50p coin |
| 2 x 20p coins |
| 1 x 5p coin |
| 1 x 2p coin |
| 1 x 1p coin |

**(d)**

Does the amount of cash in the petty cash tin reconcile with the balance in the petty cash book?

Tick the correct option.

✔

| | |
|---|---|
| Yes, the amount of cash in the petty cash tin reconciles with the balance in the petty cash book | |
| No, there is not enough cash in the petty cash tin | |
| No, there is too much cash in the petty cash tin | |

**(e)**

At the end of the week what is the amount of cash that would have to be withdrawn from the bank to restore the imprest level of £100?

£ 

**(f)**

Indicate whether the following statements are true or false by ticking in the appropriate column.

| | True ✔ | False ✔ |
|---|---|---|
| A petty cash voucher is used to record individual cash payments from petty cash | | |
| A general ledger account called Petty Cash Control is used when the petty cash book is part of the double-entry system | | |
| The imprest amount is always restored to the same level | | |
| VAT can only be entered in the petty cash book if a receipt showing a separate VAT amount is provided | | |

**Task 6**

Below is a list of balances to be transferred to the trial balance.

Place the figures in the debit or credit column, as appropriate, and total each column.

Do not enter figures with decimal places in this task.

**Trial balance as at 30 June**

| Account name | Amount £ | Debit £ | Credit £ |
|---|---|---|---|
| Fixtures and fittings | 15,750 | | |
| Bank overdraft | 1,092 | | |
| Petty cash | 100 | | |
| Inventory | 9,578 | | |
| Capital | 30,000 | | |
| Drawings | 19,028 | | |
| VAT owing to HMRC | 3,753 | | |
| Loan from bank | 8,250 | | |
| Purchases | 134,076 | | |
| Sales ledger control | 43,982 | | |
| Purchases returns | 2,021 | | |
| Sales | 202,338 | | |
| Purchases ledger control | 15,102 | | |
| Sales returns | 3,260 | | |
| Discount taken (received) | 1,341 | | |
| Discount given (allowed) | 1,063 | | |
| Administration expenses | 15,122 | | |
| Advertising | 5,441 | | |
| Bank interest paid | 2,694 | | |
| Vehicle expenses | 3,599 | | |
| Office expenses | 3,116 | | |
| Rent and rates | 7,452 | | |
| Bank interest received | 360 | | |
| Totals | – | | |

**Task 7**

**(a)**

A supply of goods has been delivered to GWW Trading by Atlanta Equipment. The purchase order sent from GWW Trading, and the invoice from Atlanta Equipment, are shown below. Atlanta Equipment offers 3% settlement discount for payment within 14 days.

---

## PURCHASE ORDER
**GWW Trading**

**No** P1123
**Date** 01 06 20-4

75 Saffron Hill, Georgetown, GE7 2AA

---

To: Atlanta Equipment

Please supply 80 units of product code J48

Purchase price: £5.25 each, plus VAT @ 20%

---

## Atlanta Equipment
Savannah Street
Chatham
CH1 3TH

VAT Registration No. 892 1388 05

| GWW Trading 75 Saffron Hill Georgetown GE7 2AA | | | Invoice no. 13/456 Date: 15 July 20-4 | | |
|---|---|---|---|---|---|
| **Quantity** | **Description** | **Unit price £** | **Total £** | **Trade discount £** | **Net amount £** |
| 80 | Product J48 | 5.25 | 420.00 | 0.00 | 420.00 |
| Terms: 3% discount for payment within 14 days | | | | VAT | 84.00 |
| | | | | Total | 504.00 |

Check the invoice against the purchase order and answer the following questions:

| | |
|---|---|
| Have the correct goods been invoiced? Yes or No. | |
| Has the correct discount been applied? Yes or No. | |
| Is the VAT amount correct? If not, what should it be? | |
| What is the correct total for the invoice? | |

**(b)**

Shown below is a statement of account received from Atlanta Equipment together with the supplier's account in the purchases ledger of GWW Trading.

### Atlanta Equipment
Savannah Street

Chatham, CH1 3TH

## STATEMENT OF ACCOUNT

To: GWW Trading                                              Date: 30 June 20-4

| Date | Reference number | Details | Amount £ | Amount £ | Balance £ |
|---|---|---|---|---|---|
| 3 May | 6188 | Goods | 552 | | 552 |
| 12 May | 6190 | Goods | 110 | | 662 |
| 18 May | 6225 | Goods | 210 | | 872 |
| 26 May | 6263 | Goods | 227 | | 1,099 |
| 1 June | | Payment | | 662 | 437 |

| Atlanta Equipment | | | | | |
|---|---|---|---|---|---|
| Date | Details | Amount £ | Date | Details | Amount £ |
| 1 June | Bank | 662 | 3 May | Purchases | 552 |
| 29 June | Bank | 227 | 12 May | Purchases | 110 |
| | | | 26 May | Purchases | 227 |

Which item is missing from the statement of account from Atlanta Equipment? Select your answer from the following list:

Invoice 6188, invoice 6190, invoice 6225, invoice 6263, payment for £662, payment for £227.

|  |
|---|

**(c)**

Which item is missing from the supplier account in GWW's purchases ledger? Select your answer from the following list:

Invoice 6188, invoice 6190, invoice 6225, invoice 6263, payment for £662, payment for £227.

|  |
|---|

**(d)**

Assuming any differences between the statement from Atlanta Equipment and the supplier account in GWW's purchases ledger are simply due to omission errors, what is the amount owing to Atlanta Equipment?

| £ |
|---|

**Task 8**

**(a)**

| **GWW Trading** |
|---|
| 75 Saffron Hill |
| Georgetown |
| GE7 2AA |

| Ashley Supplies<br>Gettysburg Drive<br>Georgetown<br>GE8 4TP | Delivery note  6691<br><br>Purchase order no. 10/F73<br><br>Date: 10 July 20-4 |
|---|---|

| Quantity | Description |
|---|---|
| 5 | T82 Genus cells (product code A4 - T82) |

Signed for by (signature) .....*E Jones*................ Print name ...Ellie Jones.....................................

The price of the cells was £156.25 each plus VAT at 20%. Ashley Supplies are to be given a 20% trade discount.

Complete the sales invoice below.

| | | | GWW Trading | | | |
|---|---|---|---|---|---|---|
| | | | 75 Saffron Hill | | | |
| | | | Georgetown | | | |
| | | | GE7 2AA | | | |
| | | | VAT Registration No. 330 1415 09 | | | |

| Date: 12 July 20-4 | | | | Sales invoice no. 66068 | | |
|---|---|---|---|---|---|---|
| Customer account code: ASHLEY | | | | Purchase order no. 10/F73 | | |

| Quantity | Product code | Price each £ | Total £ | Trade discount £ | Goods £ |
|---|---|---|---|---|---|
| | | | | | |
| | | | | | |

| Terms: net monthly | VAT | |
|---|---|---|
| | Total | |

**(b)**

One of the cells was found to be faulty and was returned to GWW by Ashley Supplies. Select the correct total (including VAT) for the credit note due.

✔

| | |
|---|---|
| £156.25 | |
| £187.50 | |
| £125.00 | |
| £150.00 | |

**(c)**

The account for R Butler Ltd shown below is in the sales ledger of GWW Trading. A payment for £579 was received from this customer on 30 June.

| R Butler Ltd | | | | | |
|---|---|---|---|---|---|
| **Date 20-4** | **Details** | **Amount £** | **Date 20-4** | **Details** | **Amount £** |
| 1 May | Balance b/d | 1,693 | 5 May | Bank | 1,693 |
| 15 May | Invoice 1194 | 612 | 25 May | Credit note 391 | 33 |
| 30 May | Invoice 1202 | 792 | | | |

Which item has not been included in the payment?  Select your answer from the following list:

Balance b/d, invoice 1194, invoice 1202, Bank, credit note 391.

| |
|---|
| |

**(d)**

An invoice is being prepared by GWW Trading to be sent to R Butler Ltd. The total amount after trade discount and before VAT is £550 and the VAT rate is 20%.  A settlement discount of 2% is offered to this customer for payment within 10 days.

What is the amount GWW should receive if payment is made within 10 days?

| £ |
|---|

**(e)**

What is the amount GWW should receive if payment is NOT made within 10 days?

| £ |
|---|

**Task 9**

M Mitchell is a new customer of GWW Trading. His sales ledger account is shown below at the close of business on 30 June.

**You are to:**

**(a)**

Insert the balance carried down together with the date and details.

**(b)**

Insert the totals.

**(c)**

Insert the balance brought down together with the date and details.

| | | | M Mitchell | | |
|---|---|---|---|---|---|
| **Date 20-4** | **Details** | **Amount £** | **Date 20-4** | **Details** | **Amount £** |
| 4 June | Invoice 1423 | 79 | 12 June | Credit note 131 | 36 |
| 21 June | Invoice 1470 | 118 | 28 June | Bank | 43 |
| 25 June | Invoice 1501 | 152 | | | |
| | | | | | |
| | | | | | |

**(d)**

Complete the statement below.

Select your entries for the Details column from the following list:

Balance b/f, Credit note 131, Invoice 1423, Invoice 1470, Invoice 1501, Bank.

<table>
<tr><td colspan="4"> **GWW Trading**<br>75 Saffron Hill<br>Georgetown<br>GE7 2AA<br>STATEMENT OF ACCOUNT </td></tr>
<tr><td colspan="2">To: M Mitchell</td><td colspan="2">Date: 30 June 20-4</td></tr>
<tr><td>**Date 20-4**</td><td>**Details**</td><td>**Transaction amount £**</td><td>**Outstanding amount £**</td></tr>
<tr><td>4 June</td><td></td><td></td><td></td></tr>
<tr><td>12 June</td><td></td><td></td><td></td></tr>
<tr><td>21 June</td><td></td><td></td><td></td></tr>
<tr><td>25 June</td><td></td><td></td><td></td></tr>
<tr><td>28 June</td><td></td><td></td><td></td></tr>
</table>

**Task 10**

(a)

Show whether the following types of transaction are classified as capital income, revenue income, capital expenditure or revenue expenditure by ticking the appropriate column.

| Item | Capital income ✔ | Revenue income ✔ | Capital expenditure ✔ | Revenue expenditure ✔ |
|---|---|---|---|---|
| Receipts from cash sales | | | | |
| Receipt from sale of fittings | | | | |
| Payment of telephone bill | | | | |
| Purchase of delivery vehicle | | | | |
| Purchase of goods for resale | | | | |
| Petty cash payment for travel expenses | | | | |

(b)

Is a Bank Control account part of the double-entry bookkeeping system?

Tick the correct option.

| | ✔ |
|---|---|
| Yes | |
| No | |

**(c)**

Show whether the following statements are true or false.

| Statement | True ✔ | False ✔ |
|---|---|---|
| The Capital Account has a credit balance | | |
| An asset account has a debit balance | | |
| A liability account has a debit balance | | |

**(d)**

Classify each of the following items as an asset or a liability.

| Item | Asset ✔ | Liability ✔ |
|---|---|---|
| Office equipment | | |
| VAT owed to HMRC | | |
| Money owed to trade payables | | |

**(e)**

GWW Trading codes all purchase invoices with a supplier account code and a general ledger code.

A selection of supplier account codes used is given below.

| Supplier | Supplier account code |
|---|---|
| Atlanta Equipment | ATLANT |
| Twelve Oaks Ltd | TWELVE |
| D Charles | CHARLE |
| Meade Lodge | MEADE |
| Yankee Supplies | YANKEE |

What code would be given to a new supplier called Bonnie Ltd?

| |
|---|

**(f)**

A selection of general ledger codes used is given below.

| Item | General ledger code |
|---|---|
| Cells | GL25 |
| Plant | GL30 |
| Stone | GL26 |
| Timber | GL32 |
| Metal | GL23 |

During the month GWW Trading receives a number of supplier invoices.

Enter the appropriate supplier and general ledger codes in the table below. Refer to the supplier and general ledger codes given above.

| Supplier | Product | Supplier account code | General ledger code |
|---|---|---|---|
| Twelve Oaks Ltd | Granite stone | | |
| Yankee Supplies | Plant | | |
| Atlanta Equipment | Metal rods | | |
| D Charles | Timber poles | | |
| Meade Lodge | Cells | | |
| D Charles | Steel and iron | | |

# Practice
# assessment 3

Complete all 10 tasks.

Each task is independent.  You will not need to refer to your answers in previous tasks.

The tasks are set in a business where the following apply:

- You are employed by the business, Lympstone Ltd, as a bookkeeper.

- Lympstone Ltd uses a manual bookkeeping system.

- Double-entry takes place in the general ledger.  Individual accounts of trade receivables and trade payables are kept in the sales and purchases ledgers as subsidiary accounts.

- The cash book and petty cash book should be treated as part of the  double-entry system unless the task instructions state otherwise.

- The VAT rate is 20%.

**Task 1**

Sales invoices and sales credit notes have been received and partially entered in the day books, as shown below.

Complete the entries in the sales day book and the sales returns day book by:

- inserting the correct customer account codes from the coding list below

- inserting the appropriate figures to complete the entries

- enter totals for 30 June

| Coding list | |
|---|---|
| Beacon Trading | B001 |
| Brent Tools | B002 |
| Bow Street DIY | B003 |
| Cameron Ltd | C001 |
| Crossways Ltd | C002 |
| Durning Ltd | D001 |
| M Khan | K001 |
| C Perrett | P001 |
| Quay Supplies | Q001 |
| Zelah plc | Z001 |

**Sales day book**

| Date 20-4 | Details | Account code | Invoice number | Total £ | VAT £ | Net £ | Sales type 1 £ | Sales type 2 £ |
|---|---|---|---|---|---|---|---|---|
| 30 Jun | Durning Ltd | | 1520 | 1,104 | | | 690 | 230 |
| 30 Jun | C Perrett | | 1521 | | 696 | | | 3,480 |
| 30 Jun | Beacon Trading | | 1522 | | | 5,040 | 5,040 | |
| 30 Jun | Zelah plc | | 1523 | 2,256 | | | 993 | 887 |
| | | | Totals | | | | | |

**Sales returns day book**

| Date 20-4 | Details | Account code | Credit note number | Total £ | VAT £ | Net £ | Sales type 1 £ | Sales type 2 £ |
|---|---|---|---|---|---|---|---|---|
| 30 Jun | Quay Supplies | | 292 | | 7 | | | 35 |
| 30 Jun | Brent Tools | | 293 | | | 295 | 295 | |
| | | | Totals | | | | | |

**Task 2**

The following credit transactions have been entered into the purchases day book as shown below. No entries have yet been made into the ledgers.

**Purchases day book**

| Date 20-4 | Details | Invoice number | Total £ | VAT £ | Net £ |
|---|---|---|---|---|---|
| 30 Jun | Mithian & Co | 1684 | 816 | 136 | 680 |
| 30 Jun | Bolster Stores | 414 | 528 | 88 | 440 |
| | | Totals | 1,344 | 224 | 1,120 |

**(a)**

What will be the entries in the subsidiary purchases ledger?

Select your account names from the following list: Bolster Stores, Mithian & Co, Purchases, Purchases ledger control, Purchases returns, Sales, Sales ledger control, Sales returns, VAT.

Enter the names and amounts and tick the appropriate debit or credit column.

**Purchases ledger**

| Account name | Amount £ | Debit ✔ | Credit ✔ |
|---|---|---|---|
|  |  |  |  |
|  |  |  |  |

**(b)**

What will be the entries in the general ledger?

Select your account names from the following list: Bolster Stores, Mithian & Co, Purchases, Purchases ledger control, Purchases returns, Sales, Sales ledger control, Sales returns, VAT.

Enter the names and amounts and tick the appropriate debit or credit column.

**General ledger**

| Account name | Amount £ | Debit ✔ | Credit ✔ |
|---|---|---|---|
|  |  |  |  |
|  |  |  |  |
|  |  |  |  |

## Task 3

The following receipts are to be entered in the debit side of Lympstone Ltd's cash book on one day.

1　Cash received from cash sales: £420 including VAT at 20%.

2　Cheque received for £777 from Brent Tools in payment of their account. This includes settlement discount of £13.

3　Bank receipt for £426 from Cameron Ltd in payment of their account. This includes settlement discount of £7.

**(a)**

Make entries in the relevant columns of the debit side of the cash book shown below.

Select your entries for the Details column from the following list:

Bank, Brent Tools, Cameron Ltd, Cash, Cash sales, Discount, Trade receivables, VAT.

**(b)**

Total each column.

**Cash book – debit side**

| Details | Discount £ | Cash £ | Bank £ | VAT £ | Trade receivables £ | Cash sales £ |
|---|---|---|---|---|---|---|
| Balance b/f | | 256 | | | | |
| | | | | | | |
| | | | | | | |
| | | | | | | |
| Totals | | | | | | |

**(c)**

The credit side of the cash book shows total cash paid out of £432 on the same day.

Using your answers above, calculate the cash balance at the end of the day.

£ [          ]

**(d)**

The credit side of the cash book shows an overdraft brought forward at the beginning of the day of £501 and other bank payments on the day of £198.

Using your answers above, calculate the bank balance. If your calculations show that the bank account is overdrawn, your answer should start with a minus sign, for example –123.

£ [          ]

## Task 4

Lympstone Ltd's cash book is both a book of prime entry and part of the double-entry bookkeeping system.  These are the totals of the columns in the credit side of the cash book at the end of the month.

**Cash book - credit side**

| Details | Discount £ | Cash £ | Bank £ | VAT £ | Trade payables £ | Office expenses £ | Premises expenses £ |
|---|---|---|---|---|---|---|---|
| Totals | 250 | 2,136 | 14,722 | 356 | 14,722 | 956 | 824 |

**(a)**

What will be the **SIX** entries in the general ledger?

Select your account names from the following list:  Bank, Cash, Cash purchases, Discount given, Discount taken, Office expenses, Premises expenses, Purchases ledger control, Sales ledger control, Trade payables, VAT.

Enter the names and amounts and tick the appropriate debit or credit column.

**General ledger**

| Account name | Amount £ | Debit ✔ | Credit ✔ |
|---|---|---|---|
|  |  |  |  |
|  |  |  |  |
|  |  |  |  |
|  |  |  |  |
|  |  |  |  |
|  |  |  |  |

**(b)**

One of the bank payments to trade payables was to Expo Products for £306. This included settlement discount of £8.

What will be the **TWO** entries in the purchases ledger?

Select your account names from the following list: Bank, Expo Products, Lympstone Ltd, Purchases, Purchases ledger, Purchases ledger control, Sales, Sales ledger, Sales ledger control, Trade payables.

Enter the names and amounts and tick the appropriate debit or credit column.

| Account name | Amount £ | Debit ✔ | Credit ✔ |
|---|---|---|---|
| | | | |
| | | | |

## Task 5

Lympstone Ltd maintains a petty cash book as both a book of prime entry and part of the double-entry accounting system. The following transactions all took place on 30 June and have been entered in the petty cash book as shown below. No entries have yet been made in the general ledger.

**(a)**

Total the analysis columns and insert the balance carried down.

**Petty cash book**

| Date 20-4 | Details | Amount £ | Date 20-4 | Details | Amount £ | VAT £ | Postage £ | Travel expenses £ | Office expenses £ |
|---|---|---|---|---|---|---|---|---|---|
| 30 Jun | Balance b/f | 94.00 | 30 Jun | Stationery | 24.48 | 4.08 | | | 20.40 |
| 30 Jun | Bank | 56.00 | 30 Jun | Post office | 12.00 | | 12.00 | | |
| | | | 30 Jun | Rail fare | 20.50 | | | 20.50 | |
| | | | 30 Jun | Printer supplies | 26.40 | 4.40 | | | 22.00 |
| | | | | Balance c/d | | | | | |
| | | 150.00 | | | 150.00 | | | | |

**(b)**

What will be the **FIVE** entries in the general ledger?

Select your account names from the following list: Balance b/f, Balance c/d, Bank, Office expenses, Petty cash book, Postage, Post office, Printer supplies, Rail fare, Stationery, Travel expenses, VAT.

Enter the names and amounts and tick the appropriate debit or credit column.

**General ledger**

| Account name | Amount £ | Debit ✔ | Credit ✔ |
|---|---|---|---|
| | | | |
| | | | |
| | | | |
| | | | |
| | | | |

**(c)**

Complete the following statements about petty cash. Choose one of the options in the boxes below to fill each gap.

| | | | |
|---|---|---|---|
| balancing | bank statement | non-imprest | petty cash voucher |

| | | | |
|---|---|---|---|
| amount of cash in the petty cash tin | petty cash | reconciliation | imprest |

1. The balance of the petty cash book should be checked regularly against the

   |  |
   |--|
   |  |

   This is called

   |  |
   |--|
   |  |

2. If the amount in the petty cash tin is always topped up to the same level, the system is called

   |  |
   |--|
   |  |

3. Petty cash payments are recorded on a document called a

   |  |
   |--|
   |  |

**Task 6**

Below is a list of balances to be transferred to the trial balance as at 30 June.

Place the figures in the debit or credit column, as appropriate, and total each column.

| Account name | Amount £ | Debit £ | Credit £ |
|---|---|---|---|
| Vehicles | 15,390 | | |
| Bank overdraft | 1,270 | | |
| Petty cash control | 112 | | |
| Inventory | 9,345 | | |
| Capital | 31,796 | | |
| Drawings | 6,290 | | |
| VAT owing to HM Revenue & Customs | 2,317 | | |
| Loan from bank | 5,650 | | |
| Purchases | 22,685 | | |
| Sales ledger control | 8,351 | | |
| Purchases returns | 1,248 | | |
| Sales | 46,854 | | |
| Purchases ledger control | 6,382 | | |
| Sales returns | 1,685 | | |
| Discount received | 817 | | |
| Discount allowed | 621 | | |
| Administration | 18,341 | | |
| Premises expenses | 4,057 | | |
| Office expenses | 1,298 | | |
| Heating and lighting | 1,836 | | |
| Rent and rates | 3,494 | | |
| Travel costs | 1,022 | | |
| Telephone | 874 | | |
| Postage | 933 | | |
| Totals | – | | |

**Task 7**

A supply of batteries has been delivered to Lympstone Ltd by Electrical Supplies. The purchase order sent from Lympstone Ltd, and the invoice from Electrical Supplies, are shown below.

---

# Lympstone Ltd

29 Constitution Street

Mereford, MR11 4GT

---

Purchase Order No. ST1872

To: Electrical Supplies

Date: 9 July 20-4

Please supply 200 packs of AA batteries product code 6543AA

Purchase price: £5 per pack, plus VAT

Discount: less 25% trade discount, as agreed.

---

**INVOICE**                    **Electrical Supplies**

Unit 16 Varsity Estate, Spirefield SP6 3DF

VAT Registration No. 118 3822 39

Invoice No. 2363
Lympstone Ltd
29 Constitution Street
Mereford, MR11 4GT

12 July 20-4

| | | |
|---|---|---|
| 200 | Packs AA batteries @ £5.00 per pack less trade discount | £800.00 |
| | VAT @ 20% | £160.00 |
| | Total | £960.00 |

Terms: 30 days net

**(a)**

Check the invoice against the purchase order and answer the following questions.

| | |
|---|---|
| Has the correct purchase price of the batteries been charged? Yes or No? | |
| Has the correct discount been applied? Yes or No? | |
| What would be the VAT amount charged if the invoice was correct? | |
| What would be the total amount charged if the invoice was correct? | |

**(b)**

Shown below is a statement of account received from G French & Co, a credit supplier, and the supplier's account as shown in the purchases ledger of Lympstone Ltd.

## G French & Co

### 17 Highfield Grove, West Mereford, MR2 7GH

To: Lympstone Ltd

29 Constitution Street

Mereford, MR11 4GT            **STATEMENT OF ACCOUNT**

| Date 20-4 | Invoice Number | Details | Invoice Amount £ | Cheque Amount £ | Balance £ |
|---|---|---|---|---|---|
| 1 June | 1685 | Goods | 8,000 | | 8,000 |
| 2 June | 1687 | Goods | 2,600 | | 10,600 |
| 8 June | 1696 | Goods | 700 | | 11,300 |
| 26 June | 1752 | Goods | 1,500 | | 12,800 |
| 1 July | - | Cheque | | 8,000 | 4,800 |

| | | | G French & Co | | | |
|---|---|---|---|---|---|---|
| Date 20-4 | Details | | Amount £ | Date 20-4 | Details | Amount £ |
| 1 July | Bank | | 8,000 | 1 June | Purchases | 8,000 |
| 25 July | Bank | | 4,000 | 7 June | Purchases | 2,600 |
| | | | | 10 June | Purchases | 700 |

**(1)**   Which item is missing from the statement of account from G French & Co?

Select your answer from the following list: Invoice 1685, Invoice 1687, Invoice 1696, Invoice 1752, Cheque for £8,000, Cheque for £4,000.

> [                    ]

**(2)**   Which item is missing from the supplier account in Lympstone Ltd's purchases ledger?

Select your answer from the following list: Invoice 1685, Invoice 1687, Invoice 1696, Invoice 1752, Cheque for £8,000, Cheque for £4,000.

> [                    ]

**(3)**   Assuming any differences between the statement of account from G French & Co and the supplier account in Lympstone Ltd's purchases ledger are simply due to omission errors, what is the amount owing to G French & Co?

> £ [                    ]

**Task 8**

On 1 July Lympstone Ltd delivered the following goods to a credit customer, Bow Street DIY.

| **Lympstone Ltd** |
| 29 Constitution Street |
| Mereford, MR11 4GT |

| Delivery note No. 21765 | Date: 9 July 20-4 |
|---|---|
| Bow Street DIY | Customer account code: BS152 |
| 20 Penarth Road | |
| Bow Street | |
| Ceredigion, SY56 2AW | |

10 Supathrust Power Drill product code PD124.

The list price of the drills was £56 each plus VAT at 20%. Bow Street DIY are to be given a 20% trade discount and a 5% early settlement discount.

**(a)**

**(1)**  Complete the invoice below.

<table>
<tr><td colspan="6" align="center"><br>**Lympstone Ltd**<br><br>29 Constitution Street<br><br>Mereford, MR11 4GT<br><br>VAT Registration No. 298 3827 04<br></td></tr>
<tr><td colspan="3">Bow Street DIY<br>20 Penarth Road<br>Bow Street<br>Ceredigion, SY56 2AW<br><br>Invoice No: 1298</td><td colspan="3">Customer account code:<br><br>Delivery note number:<br><br>Date: 9 July 20-4</td></tr>
<tr><td>**Quantity**</td><td>**Code**</td><td>**Unit price**<br>£</td><td>**Total**<br>£</td><td>**Net amount**<br>£</td><td>**VAT(20%)**<br>£</td><td>**Gross**<br>£</td></tr>
<tr><td></td><td></td><td></td><td></td><td></td><td></td><td></td></tr>
</table>

**(2)**  What would be the amount payable on this invoice if the settlement (cash) discount was taken by Bow Street DIY?

Select your answer from the following options:  ✔

| | |
|---|---|
| £448.00 | |
| £510.72 | |
| £533.12 | |
| £672.00 | |

**(b)**

The account shown below is in the sales ledger of Lympstone Ltd. A cheque for £1,300 was received from this customer on 2 July.

| M Khan | | | | | |
|---|---|---|---|---|---|
| Date 20-4 | Details | Amount £ | Date 20-4 | Details | Amount £ |
| 1 June | Balance b/f | 4,620 | 2 June | Bank | 4,620 |
| 22 June | Sales invoice 1201 | 1,962 | 26 June | Sales returns credit note 295 | 662 |
| 30 June | Sales invoice 1262 | 2,850 | | | |

**(1)**   Which item has not been included in the payment?

Select your account name from the following list: Balance b/f, Sales invoice 1201, Sales invoice 1262, Bank, Sales returns credit note 295.

[                    ]

**(2)**   A further sales invoice was issued to M Khan for £2,340 on 2 July. What was the amount outstanding on the account on 3 July? No further payments had been received or other transactions made since 30 June.

£ [            ]

**(3)**   Lympstone Ltd on 1 July offered M Khan an extra discount of 5% on invoices of value of £3,000 or more. This is known as:

✔

| | |
|---|---|
| Settlement discount | |
| Trade discount | |
| Bulk discount | |

**Task 9**

The following customer account is in the sales ledger at the close of business on 30 June.

**(a)**

Insert the balance carried down together with the date and details.

**(b)**

Insert the totals.

**(c)**

Insert the balance brought down together with the date and details.

<table>
<tr><th colspan="6">Crossways Ltd</th></tr>
<tr><th>Date 20-4</th><th>Details</th><th>Amount £</th><th>Date 20-4</th><th>Details</th><th>Amount £</th></tr>
<tr><td>1 June</td><td>Balance b/d</td><td>530</td><td>21 June</td><td>Credit note 285</td><td>125</td></tr>
<tr><td>10 June</td><td>Invoice 1459</td><td>450</td><td>30 June</td><td>Bank</td><td>405</td></tr>
<tr><td>12 June</td><td>Invoice 1470</td><td>1,210</td><td></td><td></td><td></td></tr>
<tr><td>27 June</td><td>Invoice 1500</td><td>720</td><td></td><td></td><td></td></tr>
<tr><td></td><td></td><td></td><td></td><td></td><td></td></tr>
<tr><td></td><td></td><td></td><td></td><td></td><td></td></tr>
</table>

**(d)**

Complete the statement below.

Select your entries for the Details column from the following list: Balance b/f, Credit note 285, Invoice 1459, Invoice 1470, Invoice 1500, Payment.

| | **Lympstone Ltd** | | |
|---|---|---|---|
| | 29 Constitution Street | | |
| | Mereford, MR11 4GT | | |
| | STATEMENT OF ACCOUNT | | |
| To: Crossways Ltd | | Date: 30 June 20-4 | |
| **Date 20-4** | **Details** | **Transaction amount** £ | **Outstanding amount** £ |
| 1 June | | | |
| 10 June | | | |
| 12 June | | | |
| 21 June | | | |
| 27 June | | | |
| 30 June | | | |

## Task 10

Financial accounting is based upon the accounting equation.

**(a)**

Show whether the following statements are true or false.

| Statement | True ✔ | False ✔ |
|---|---|---|
| Assets equals capital plus liabilities | | |
| Capital equals assets plus liabilities | | |
| Assets minus liabilities equals capital | | |

**(b)**

Classify each of the following items as an asset or a liability.

| Item | Asset ✔ | Liability ✔ |
|---|---|---|
| Bank overdraft | | |
| Office equipment | | |
| Money owing to payables | | |

**(c)**

Lympstone Ltd codes all purchase invoices with a supplier code and a general ledger code. A selection of the codes used is given below.

| Supplier | Supplier Account Code |
|---|---|
| Delta Ltd | DEL08 |
| Electrical Supplies | ELE10 |
| Elemox & Co | ELE14 |
| Expo Products | EXP04 |
| Faraday Ltd | FAR02 |

| Item | General Ledger Code |
|---|---|
| Electrical goods | GL380 |
| Tools | GL385 |
| Timber | GL390 |
| Paints | GL395 |
| Plumbing | GL400 |

This is an invoice received from a supplier.

---

**INVOICE**                                    **Electrical Supplies**

Unit 16 Varsity Estate, Spirefield SP6 3DF

VAT Registration No. 118 3822 39

Invoice No. 2370
Lympstone Ltd
29 Constitution Street
Mereford, MR11 4GT

22 July 20-4

| | | |
|---|---|---:|
| 50 | Screwdriver sets @ £2.40 each less trade discount | £90.00 |
| | VAT @ 20% | £ 18.00 |
| | Total | £108.00 |

---

Select which codes would be used to code this invoice.

**(1)**

Select your supplier account code from the following list: DEL08, ELE10, ELE14, EXP04, FAR02, GL380, GL385, GL390, GL395, GL400.

| |
|---|
| |

**(2)**

Select your general ledger account code from the following list: DEL08, ELE10, ELE14, EXP04, FAR02, GL380, GL385, GL390, GL395, GL400.

| |
|---|
| |

**(3)**

State which two codes would be used if the supply had been made by Expo Products and had been a consignment of gloss paint.

| |
|---|
| |

**(d)**

Income and expenditure classifications are shown on the left below. Link each transaction example shown on the right to its correct classification by joining the boxes.

| | |
|---|---|
| Capital income | Sale of goods manufactured |
| | Payment of electricity bill |
| Capital expenditure | Sale of property |
| | Purchase of production machinery |
| Revenue income | Purchase of inventory |
| Revenue expenditure | Receipt from cash sales |

# Practice assessment 1 answers

**Task 1**

**Purchases day book**

| Date 20-4 | Details | Supplier Account Code | Invoice number | Total £ | VAT £ | Net £ | Purchases A £ | Purchases B £ |
|---|---|---|---|---|---|---|---|---|
| 30 Jun | A P Morleigh | MOR002 | CRO846 | 336 | 56 | 280 | | 280 |
| 30 Jun | Loddiwell Bros | LOD001 | 1532 | 2,904 | 484 | 2,420 | 420 | 2,000 |
| 30 Jun | Modbury Ltd | MOD001 | 4591 | 1,296 | 216 | 1,080 | 1,080 | |

**Purchases returns day book**

| Date 20-4 | Details | Supplier Account Code | Credit note number | Total £ | VAT £ | Net £ | Purchases A £ | Purchases B £ |
|---|---|---|---|---|---|---|---|---|
| 30 Jun | Torcross plc | TOR001 | 7511 | 840 | 140 | 700 | 700 | |
| 30 Jun | Malborough Partners | MAL003 | 10697 | 168 | 28 | 140 | 30 | 110 |

**Task 2**

**(a)**

**Sales ledger**

| Account name | Amount £ | Debit | Credit |
|---|---|---|---|
| Avon & Co | 288 | | ✔ |
| Portlemouth Ltd | 744 | | ✔ |

**(b)**

**General ledger**

| Account name | Amount £ | Debit | Credit |
|---|---|---|---|
| Sales returns | 860 | ✔ | |
| VAT | 172 | ✔ | |
| Sales ledger control | 1,032 | | ✔ |

**Task 3**

(a) and (b)

**Cash book – credit side**

| Details | Discount | Cash | Bank | VAT | Trade payables | Cash purchases |
|---|---|---|---|---|---|---|
| | £ | £ | £ | £ | £ | £ |
| Balance b/f | | | 4,720 | | | |
| Alvington Supplies | | 180 | | 30 | | 150 |
| Halwell Ltd | 45 | | 2,106 | | 2,106 | |
| Frogmore & Co | 30 | | 1,164 | | 1,164 | |
| Totals | 75 | 180 | 7,990 | 30 | 3,270 | 150 |

(c)

| £482 |
|---|

(d)

| £–2649 |
|---|

**Task 4**

(a)

**General ledger**

| Account name | Amount £ | Debit | Credit |
|---|---|---|---|
| Discount taken | 159 | | ✔ |
| VAT | 108 | ✔ | |
| Purchases ledger control | 15,928 | ✔ | |
| Purchases ledger control | 159 | ✔ | |
| Cash purchases | 540 | ✔ | |
| Bank charges | 52 | ✔ | |

(b)

**Purchases ledger**

| Account name | Amount £ | Debit | Credit |
|---|---|---|---|
| H King | 254 | ✔ | |

**Task 5**

**(a) and (b)**

**Petty cash book**

| Details | Amount £ | Details | Amount £ | VAT £ | Office expenses £ | Cleaning £ |
|---|---|---|---|---|---|---|
| Balance b/f | 100.00 | Postage | 40.00 | | 40.00 | |
| | | A4 Paper | 24.00 | 4.00 | 20.00 | |
| | | Window cleaning | 10.00 | | | 10.00 |
| | | Balance c/d | 26.00 | | | |
| Total | 100.00 | Totals | 100.00 | 4.00 | 60.00 | 10.00 |

**(c)**

| Office expenses | ✔ |
|---|---|
| VAT | ✔ |
| Cleaning | ✔ |

**(d)**

| Yes, the amount of cash in the petty cash box reconciles with the balance in the petty cash book | ✔ |
|---|---|

**(e)**

| £74 |
|---|

**(f)**

| Amount of imprest level | ✔ |
|---|---|
| Signature of person authorising the claim | ✔ |

**Task 6**

**Trial balance as at 30 June**

| Account name | Amount | Debit | Credit |
|---|---|---|---|
| | £ | £ | £ |
| Sales | 104,693 | | 104,693 |
| Sales ledger control | 14,446 | 14,446 | |
| Sales returns | 5,279 | 5,279 | |
| Purchases | 57,254 | 57,254 | |
| Purchases ledger control | 8,516 | | 8,516 |
| Purchases returns | 821 | | 821 |
| Discount received (taken) | 881 | | 881 |
| Discount allowed (given) | 702 | 702 | |
| Rent and rates | 5,149 | 5,149 | |
| Advertising | 4,385 | 4,385 | |
| Insurance | 2,537 | 2,537 | |
| Wages | 27,234 | 27,234 | |
| Heating and lighting | 2,494 | 2,494 | |
| Office expenses | 1,754 | 1,754 | |
| Telephone | 1,976 | 1,976 | |
| Cleaning | 823 | 823 | |
| Capital | 22,262 | | 22,262 |
| Office equipment | 19,680 | 19,680 | |
| Inventory | 8,080 | 8,080 | |
| Petty cash | 100 | 100 | |
| Bank (money in bank) | 3,711 | 3,711 | |
| VAT owing to HMRC | 3,284 | | 3,284 |
| Loan from bank | 15,146 | | 15,146 |
| Totals | – | 155,604 | 155,604 |

**Task 7**

**(a)**

| Month | Amount £ | Payments to be made by |
|---|---|---|
| Transactions in April | 2,004 | 30 June |
| Transactions in May | 1,500 | 31 July |
| Transactions in June | 2,160 | 31 August |

**(b)**

| Credit note 428 | ✔ |
|---|---|
| Invoice 64962 | ✔ |

**(c)**

| Questions | Yes | No |
|---|---|---|
| Has the correct product been delivered? | ✔ | |
| Has the correct quantity been delivered? | ✔ | |
| Has the correct net price been calculated? | ✔ | |
| Has the settlement discount been applied? | | ✔ |

**(d)**

| Net amount £ | VAT amount £ | Gross amount £ |
|---|---|---|
| 900.00 | 174.60 | 1,074.60 |

**Task 8**

(a)

| Remittance advice | ✔ |
|---|---|

(b)

The cheque from Strete Ltd for £2,070 has resulted in an

| under-payment | ✔ |
|---|---|
| over-payment | |

This probably relates to

| balance b/d | |
|---|---|
| invoice 523 | ✔ |
| invoice 559 | |
| invoice 602 | |
| credit note 72 | |
| bank payment 1 June | |

In order to resolve the problem Kington Supplies should

| request a remittance advice | |
|---|---|
| request a credit note | |
| request further payment | ✔ |

from Strete Ltd for

| £810 | |
|---|---|
| £420 | ✔ |
| £174 | |

which will clear the outstanding balance.

**(c)**

| Kington Supplies | | | | | |
|---|---|---|---|---|---|
| 8 Beeching Road | | | | | |
| Kington | | | | | |
| KN7 1RR | | | | | |

| Date: 15 July 20-4 | | | Sales invoice no. 66068 | | |
|---|---|---|---|---|---|
| Customer account code: STR002 | | | Purchase order no. 908 | | |

| Quantity | Product code | Price each £ | Total £ | Trade discount £ | Goods £ |
|---|---|---|---|---|---|
| 250 | B477 | 5.00 | 1,250 | 125 | 1,125.00 |
| Terms: 2% settlement discount for payment within 7 days | | | | VAT | 220.50 |
| | | | | Total | 1,345.50 |

**Task 9**

**(a) to (c)**

| E Beeson & Sons | | | | | BEE001 |
|---|---|---|---|---|---|
| **Date 20-4** | **Details** | **Amount £** | **Date 20-4** | **Details** | **Amount £** |
| 1 June | Balance b/d | 478 | 25 June | Bank | 406 |
| 29 June | Invoice 651 | 996 | 30 June | Credit note CN29 | 72 |
| | | | 30 June | Balance c/d | 996 |
| | | 1,474 | | | 1,474 |
| 1 July | Balance b/d | 996 | | | |

**(d)**

| Kington Supplies | | | |
|---|---|---|---|
| 8 Beeching Road | | | |
| Kington | | | |
| KN7 1RR | | | |
| STATEMENT OF ACCOUNT | | | |
| To: E Beeson & Sons | | Date: 30 June | |
| **Date** | **Transaction details** | **Transaction amount £** | **Outstanding amount £** |
| 1 June | Opening balance | 478 | 478 |
| 25 June | BACS | 406 | 72 |
| 29 June | Invoice 651 | 996 | 1,068 |
| 30 June | Credit note CN29 | 72 | 996 |

**Task 10**

**(a)**

| Assets £ | Liabilities £ | Capital £ |
|---|---|---|
| 25,000 | 15,000 | 10,000 |

**(b)**

| Assets £ | Liabilities £ | Capital £ |
|---|---|---|
| 35,374 | 22,578 | 12,796 |

**(c)**

| Item | Capital income | Revenue income | Capital expenditure | Revenue expenditure |
|---|:---:|:---:|:---:|:---:|
| Received cash for goods sold | | ✔ | | |
| Purchased new machinery | | | ✔ | |
| Paid rent on premises | | | | ✔ |
| Purchased goods for resale on credit | | | | ✔ |
| Received payment from a trade receivable | | ✔ | | |
| Received cash from owner | ✔ | | | |

**(d)**

| | |
|---|:---:|
| True | |
| False | ✔ |

**(e)**

| Customer name | Customer account code |
|---|---|
| GMG Gardens | GMG001 |
| Rogers Ltd | ROG002 |
| Ross Welding Ltd | ROS001 |
| Southfield & Company | SOU002 |
| Swan Construction | SWA001 |
| Westend Builders | WES001 |
| Yellowstone Ltd | YEL001 |
| Young & Co | YOU002 |

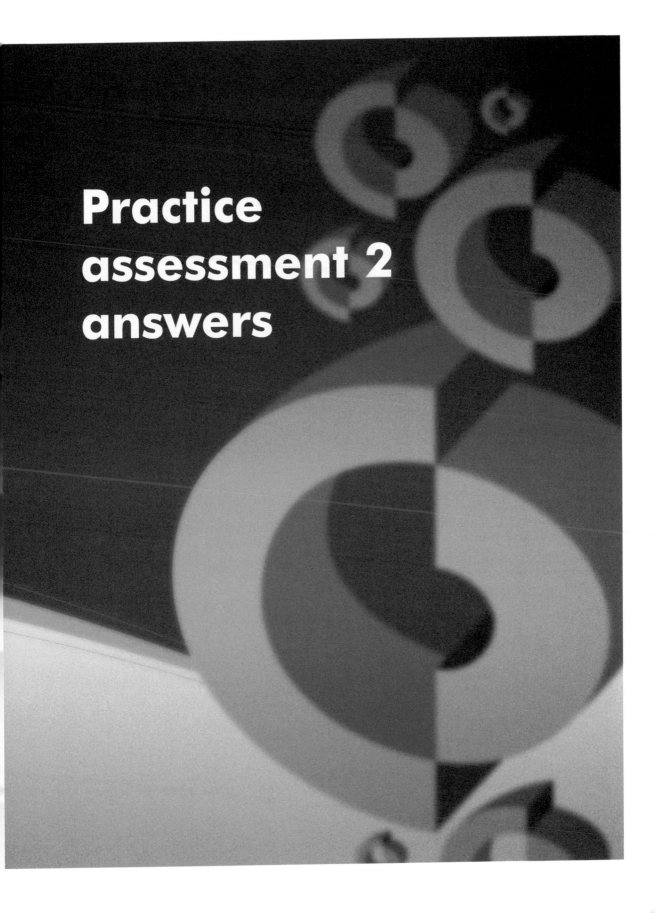

# Practice assessment 2 answers

**Task 1**

**Sales day book**

| Date 20-4 | Details | Account code | Invoice number | Total £ | VAT £ | Net £ | Sales A £ | Sales B £ |
|---|---|---|---|---|---|---|---|---|
| 30 June | Tarleton Bros | TARLET | 1530 | 780 | 130 | 650 | 650 | |
| 30 June | E Slattery Ltd | SLATTE | 1531 | 984 | 164 | 820 | | 820 |
| 30 June | Scarlet Stores | SCARLE | 1532 | 2,088 | 348 | 1,740 | 760 | 980 |

**Sales returns day book**

| Date 20-4 | Details | Account code | Credit note number | Total £ | VAT £ | Net £ | Sales A £ | Sales B £ |
|---|---|---|---|---|---|---|---|---|
| 30 June | M Hamilton plc | HAMILT | 140 | 66 | 11 | 55 | | 55 |
| 30 June | Wilkes & Son | WILKES | 141 | 234 | 39 | 195 | 195 | |

**Task 2**

**(a)**

**Purchases ledger**

| Account name | Amount £ | Debit | Credit |
|---|---|---|---|
| India Trading | 216 | ✔ | |
| Kennedy Stores | 150 | ✔ | |

**(b)**

**General ledger**

| Account name | Amount £ | Debit | Credit |
|---|---|---|---|
| Purchases returns | 305 | | ✔ |
| VAT | 61 | | ✔ |
| Purchases ledger control | 366 | ✔ | |

## Task 3

### (a) and (b)

**Cash book – debit side**

| Details | Discount £ | Cash £ | Bank £ | VAT £ | Trade receivables £ | Cash sales £ |
|---|---|---|---|---|---|---|
| Balance b/f | | 156 | 2,369 | | | |
| Cash sales | | 1,860 | | 310 | | 1,550 |
| Watling Enterprises | 50 | | 1,240 | | 1,240 | |
| O'Hara & Co | 25 | | 570 | | 570 | |
| Totals | 75 | 2,016 | 4,179 | 310 | 1,810 | 1,550 |

### (c)

£1,910

### (d)

£–2,099

## Task 4

### (a)

**General ledger**

| Account name | Amount £ | Debit | Credit |
|---|---|---|---|
| Discount given | 275 | ✔ | |
| VAT | 1,428 | | ✔ |
| Sales ledger control | 6,613 | | ✔ |
| Sales ledger control | 275 | | ✔ |
| Cash sales | 7,140 | | ✔ |
| Bank interest received | 27 | | ✔ |

### (b)

| Account name | Amount £ | Debit | Credit |
|---|---|---|---|
| R Butler Ltd | 752 | | ✔ |

## Task 5

### (a) and (b)

**Petty cash book**

| Details | Amount £ | Details | Amount £ | VAT £ | Office expenses £ | Vehicle expenses £ |
|---------|----------|---------|----------|-------|-------------------|--------------------|
| Balance b/f | 100.00 | Envelopes | 6.72 | 1.12 | 5.60 | |
| | | Stamps | 12.50 | | 12.50 | |
| | | Van repairs | 58.80 | 9.80 | | 49.00 |
| | | Balance c/d | 21.98 | | | |
| Total | 100.00 | Totals | 100.00 | 10.92 | 18.10 | 49.00 |

### (c)

| | |
|---|---|
| Office expenses | ✔ |
| VAT | ✔ |
| Vehicle expenses | ✔ |

### (d)

| | |
|---|---|
| Yes, the amount of cash in the petty cash tin reconciles with the balance in the petty cash book | ✔ |

### (e)

£78.02

### (f)

| | True | False |
|---|------|-------|
| A petty cash voucher is used to record individual cash payments from petty cash | ✔ | |
| A general ledger account called Petty Cash Control is used when the petty cash book is part of the double-entry system | | ✔ |
| The imprest amount is always restored to the same level | ✔ | |
| VAT can only be entered in the petty cash book if a receipt showing a separate VAT amount is provided | | ✔ |

**Task 6**

**Trial balance as at 30 June**

| Account name | Amount £ | Debit £ | Credit £ |
|---|---|---|---|
| Fixtures and fittings | 15,750 | 15,750 | |
| Bank overdraft | 1,092 | | 1,092 |
| Petty cash | 100 | 100 | |
| Inventory | 9,578 | 9,578 | |
| Capital | 30,000 | | 30,000 |
| Drawings | 19,028 | 19,028 | |
| VAT owing to HMRC | 3,753 | | 3,753 |
| Loan from bank | 8,250 | | 8,250 |
| Purchases | 134,076 | 134,076 | |
| Sales ledger control | 43,982 | 43,982 | |
| Purchases returns | 2,021 | | 2,021 |
| Sales | 202,338 | | 202,338 |
| Purchases ledger control | 15,102 | | 15,102 |
| Sales returns | 3,260 | 3,260 | |
| Discount taken (received) | 1,341 | | 1,341 |
| Discount given (allowed) | 1,063 | 1,063 | |
| Administration expenses | 15,122 | 15,122 | |
| Advertising | 5,441 | 5,441 | |
| Bank interest paid | 2,694 | 2,694 | |
| Vehicle expenses | 3,599 | 3,599 | |
| Office expenses | 3,116 | 3,116 | |
| Rent and rates | 7,452 | 7,452 | |
| Bank interest received | 360 | | 360 |
| Totals | – | 264,257 | 264,257 |

**Task 7**

**(a)**

| | |
|---|---|
| Have the correct goods been invoiced? Yes or No. | Yes |
| Has the correct discount been applied? Yes or No. | No |
| Is the VAT amount correct?  If not, what should it be? | £81.48 |
| What is the correct total for the invoice? | £501.48 |

**(b)**

| |
|---|
| Payment for £227 |

**(c)**

| |
|---|
| Invoice 6225 |

**(d)**

| |
|---|
| £210 |

**Task 8**

**(a)**

# GWW Trading

75 Saffron Hill

Georgetown

GE7 2AA

VAT Registration No. 330 1415 09

| Date: 12 July 20-4 | Sales invoice no. 66068 |
|---|---|
| Customer account code: ASHLEY | Purchase order no. 10/F73 |

| Quantity | Product code | Price each £ | Total £ | Trade discount £ | Goods £ |
|---|---|---|---|---|---|
| 5 | A4-T82 | 156.25 | 781.25 | 156.25 | 625.00 |
| Terms: net monthly | | | | VAT | 125.00 |
| | | | | Total | 750.00 |

**(b)**

| £150.00 | ✔ |
|---------|---|

**(c)**

| invoice 1202 |
|--------------|

**(d)**

| £646.80 |
|---------|

**(e)**

| £657.80 |
|---------|

**Task 9**

    **(a) to (c)**

<table>
<tr><td colspan="6" align="center">M Mitchell</td></tr>
<tr>
<th>Date 20-4</th>
<th>Details</th>
<th>Amount £</th>
<th>Date 20-4</th>
<th>Details</th>
<th>Amount £</th>
</tr>
<tr>
<td>4 June</td>
<td>Balance 1423</td>
<td>79</td>
<td>12 June</td>
<td>Credit note 131</td>
<td>36</td>
</tr>
<tr>
<td>21 June</td>
<td>Invoice 1470</td>
<td>118</td>
<td>28 June</td>
<td>Bank</td>
<td>43</td>
</tr>
<tr>
<td>25 June</td>
<td>Invoice 1501</td>
<td>152</td>
<td>30 June</td>
<td>Balance c/d</td>
<td>270</td>
</tr>
<tr>
<td></td>
<td></td>
<td>349</td>
<td></td>
<td></td>
<td>349</td>
</tr>
<tr>
<td>1 July</td>
<td>Balance b/d</td>
<td>270</td>
<td></td>
<td></td>
<td></td>
</tr>
</table>

**(d)**

| | **GWW Trading** | | |
| --- | --- | --- | --- |
| | 75 Saffron Hill | | |
| | Georgetown | | |
| | GE7 2AA | | |
| | STATEMENT OF ACCOUNT | | |
| To: M Mitchell | | Date: 30 June 20-4 | |
| **Date 20-4** | **Details** | **Transaction amount £** | **Outstanding amount £** |
| 4 June | Invoice 1423 | 79 | 79 |
| 12 June | Credit note 131 | 36 | 43 |
| 21 June | Invoice 1470 | 118 | 161 |
| 25 June | Invoice 1501 | 152 | 313 |
| 28 June | Bank | 43 | 270 |

**Task 10**

**(a)**

| Item | Capital income | Revenue income | Capital expenditure | Revenue expenditure |
|---|---|---|---|---|
| Receipts from cash sales | | ✔ | | |
| Receipt from sale of fittings | ✔ | | | |
| Payment of telephone bill | | | | ✔ |
| Purchase of delivery vehicle | | | ✔ | |
| Purchase of goods for resale | | | | ✔ |
| Petty cash payment for travel expenses | | | | ✔ |

**(b)**

| | |
|---|---|
| Yes | ✔ |
| No | |

**(c)**

| Statement | True | False |
|---|---|---|
| The Capital Account has a credit balance | ✔ | |
| An asset account has a debit balance | ✔ | |
| A liability account has a debit balance | | ✔ |

**(d)**

| Item | Asset | Liability |
|------|:-----:|:---------:|
| Office equipment | ✔ | |
| VAT owed to HMRC | | ✔ |
| Money owed to trade payables | | ✔ |

**(e)**

| BONNIE |
|--------|

**(f)**

| Supplier | Product | Supplier account code | General ledger code |
|----------|---------|------------------------|----------------------|
| Twelve Oaks Ltd | Granite stone | TWELVE | GL26 |
| Yankee Supplies | Plant | YANKEE | GL30 |
| Atlanta Equipment | Metal rods | ATLANT | GL23 |
| D Charles | Timber poles | CHARLE | GL32 |
| Meade Lodge | Cells | MEADE | GL25 |
| D Charles | Steel and iron | CHARLE | GL23 |

# Practice assessment 3 answers

**Task 1**

**Sales day book**

| Date 20-4 | Details | Account code | Invoice number | Total £ | VAT £ | Net £ | Sales type 1 £ | Sales type 2 £ |
|---|---|---|---|---|---|---|---|---|
| 30 Jun | Durning Ltd | D001 | 1520 | 1,104 | 184 | 920 | 690 | 230 |
| 30 Jun | C Perrett | P001 | 1521 | 4,176 | 696 | 3,480 | | 3,480 |
| 30 Jun | Beacon Trading | B001 | 1522 | 6,048 | 1,008 | 5,040 | 5,040 | |
| 30 Jun | Zelah plc | Z001 | 1523 | 2,256 | 376 | 1,880 | 993 | 887 |
| | | | Totals | 13,584 | 2,264 | 11,320 | 6,723 | 4,597 |

**Sales returns day book**

| Date 20-4 | Details | Account code | Credit note number | Total £ | VAT £ | Net £ | Sales type 1 £ | Sales type 2 £ |
|---|---|---|---|---|---|---|---|---|
| 30 Jun | Quay Supplies | Q001 | 292 | 42 | 7 | 35 | | 35 |
| 30 Jun | Brent Tools | B002 | 293 | 354 | 59 | 295 | 295 | |
| | | | Totals | 396 | 66 | 330 | 295 | 35 |

**Task 2**

**(a)**

**Purchases ledger**

| Account name | Amount £ | Debit | Credit |
|---|---|---|---|
| Mithian & Co | 816 | | ✔ |
| Bolster Stores | 528 | | ✔ |

**(b)**

**General ledger**

| Account name | Amount £ | Debit | Credit |
|---|---|---|---|
| Purchases | 1,120 | ✔ | |
| VAT | 224 | ✔ | |
| Purchases ledger control | 1,344 | | ✔ |

**Task 3**

(a) and (b)

**Cash book – debit side**

| Details | Discount £ | Cash £ | Bank £ | VAT £ | Trade receivables £ | Cash sales £ |
|---|---|---|---|---|---|---|
| Balance b/f | | 256 | | | | |
| Cash sales | | 420 | | 70 | | 350 |
| Brent Tools | 13 | | 777 | | 777 | |
| Cameron Ltd | 7 | | 426 | | 426 | |
| Totals | 20 | 676 | 1,203 | 70 | 1,203 | 350 |

(c)

| £244 |
|---|

(d)

| £504 |
|---|

**Task 4**

(a)

**General ledger**

| Account name | Amount £ | Debit | Credit |
|---|---|---|---|
| Discount taken | 250 | | ✔ |
| VAT | 356 | ✔ | |
| Purchases ledger control | 14,722 | ✔ | |
| Purchases ledger control | 250 | ✔ | |
| Office expenses | 956 | ✔ | |
| Premises expenses | 824 | ✔ | |

**(b)**

| Account name | Amount £ | Debit | Credit |
|---|---|---|---|
| Expo Products | 306 | ✔ | |
| Expo Products | 8 | ✔ | |

## Task 5

**(a)**

**Petty cash book**

| Date 20-4 | Details | Amount £ | Date 20-4 | Details | Amount £ | VAT £ | Postage £ | Travel expenses £ | Office expenses £ |
|---|---|---|---|---|---|---|---|---|---|
| 30 Jun | Balance b/f | 94.00 | 30 Jun | Stationery | 24.48 | 4.08 | | | 20.40 |
| 30 Jun | Bank | 56.00 | 30 Jun | Post office | 12.00 | | 12.00 | | |
| | | | 30 Jun | Rail fare | 20.50 | | | 20.50 | |
| | | | 30 Jun | Printer supplies | 26.40 | 4.40 | | | 22.00 |
| | | | | Balance c/d | 66.62 | | | | |
| | | 150.00 | | | 150.00 | 8.48 | 12.00 | 20.50 | 42.40 |

**(b)**

**General ledger**

| Account name | Amount £ | Debit | Credit |
|---|---|---|---|
| Value Added Tax | 8.48 | ✔ | |
| Postage | 12.00 | ✔ | |
| Travel expenses | 20.50 | ✔ | |
| Office expenses | 42.40 | ✔ | |
| Bank | 56.00 | | ✔ |

**(c)**

1.  The balance of the petty cash book should be checked regularly against the

| amount of cash in the petty cash tin |
| --- |

.

This is called

| reconciliation |
| --- |

.

2.  If the amount in the petty cash tin is always topped up to the same level, the system is called

| imprest |
| --- |

.

3.  Petty cash payments are recorded on a document called a

| petty cash voucher |
| --- |

.

**Task 6**

| Account name | Amount £ | Debit £ | Credit £ |
|---|---|---|---|
| Vehicles | 15,390 | 15,390 | |
| Bank overdraft | 1,270 | | 1,270 |
| Petty cash control | 112 | 112 | |
| Inventory | 9,345 | 9,345 | |
| Capital | 31,796 | | 31,796 |
| Drawings | 6,290 | 6,290 | |
| VAT owing to HM Revenue & Customs | 2,317 | | 2,317 |
| Loan from bank | 5,650 | | 5,650 |
| Purchases | 22,685 | 22,685 | |
| Sales ledger control | 8,351 | 8,351 | |
| Purchases returns | 1,248 | | 1,248 |
| Sales | 46,854 | | 46,854 |
| Purchases ledger control | 6,382 | | 6,382 |
| Sales returns | 1,685 | 1,685 | |
| Discount received | 817 | | 817 |
| Discount allowed | 621 | 621 | |
| Administration | 18,341 | 18,341 | |
| Premises expenses | 4,057 | 4,057 | |
| Office expenses | 1,298 | 1,298 | |
| Heating and lighting | 1,836 | 1,836 | |
| Rent and rates | 3,494 | 3,494 | |
| Travel costs | 1,022 | 1,022 | |
| Telephone | 874 | 874 | |
| Postage | 933 | 933 | |
| Totals | – | 96,334 | 96,334 |

**Task 7**

(a)

| Has the correct purchase price of the batteries been charged? | Yes |
|---|---|
| Has the correct discount been applied? | No |
| What would be the VAT amount charged if the invoice was correct? | £150.00 |
| What would be the total amount charged if the invoice was correct? | £900.00 |

(b)

(1) | Cheque for £4,000 |

(2) | Invoice 1752 |

(3) | £800.00 |

**Task 8**

(a)

(1)    Complete the invoice below.

| | | | | | | |
|---|---|---|---|---|---|---|
| | | | **Lympstone Ltd** | | | |
| | | | 29 Constitution Street | | | |
| | | | Mereford, MR11 4GT | | | |
| | | | VAT Registration No. 298 3827 04 | | | |

Bow Street DIY
20 Penarth Road
Bow Street
Ceredigion, SY56 2AW

Invoice No: 1298

Customer account code:

Delivery note number:

Date: 9 July 20-4

| Quantity | Code | Unit price £ | Total £ | Net amount £ | VAT(20%) £ | Gross £ |
|---|---|---|---|---|---|---|
| 10 | PD124 | 56.00 | 560.00 | 448.00 | 85.12 | 533.12 |

(2)

| £510.72 | ✔ |
|---|---|

(b)

(1)  | Sales invoice 1262 |

(2)  | £5,190 |

(3)  | Bulk discount | ✔ |

**Task 9**

(a) to (c)

| | | | | | |
|---|---|---|---|---|---|
| | | **Crossways Ltd** | | | |
| **Date 20-4** | **Details** | **Amount £** | **Date 20-4** | **Details** | **Amount £** |
| 1 June | Balance b/d | 530 | 21 June | Credit note 285 | 125 |
| 10 June | Invoice 1459 | 450 | 30 June | Bank | 405 |
| 12 June | Invoice 1470 | 1,210 | 30 June | Balance c/d | 2,380 |
| 27 June | Invoice 1500 | 720 | | | |
| | | 2,910 | | | 2,910 |
| 1 July | Balance b/d | 2,380 | | | |

(d)

**Lympstone Ltd**

29 Constitution Street

Mereford, MR11 4GT

STATEMENT OF ACCOUNT

To: Crossways Ltd                                        Date: 30 June 20-4

| Date 20-4 | Details | Transaction amount £ | Outstanding amount £ |
|---|---|---|---|
| 1 June | Balance b/f | | 530 |
| 10 June | Invoice 1459 | 450 | 980 |
| 12 June | Invoice 1470 | 1,210 | 2,190 |
| 21 June | Credit note 285 | 125 | 2,065 |
| 27 June | Invoice 1500 | 720 | 2,785 |
| 30 June | Payment | 405 | 2,380 |

**Task 10**

**(a)**

| Statement | True | False |
|---|---|---|
| Assets equals capital plus liabilities | ✔ | |
| Capital equals assets plus liabilities | | ✔ |
| Assets minus liabilities equals capital | ✔ | |

**(b)**

| Item | Asset | Liability |
|---|---|---|
| Bank overdraft | | ✔ |
| Office equipment | ✔ | |
| Money owing to payables | | ✔ |

**(c)**

**(1)**

| |
|---|
| ELE10 |

**(2)**

| |
|---|
| GL385 |

**(3)**

| |
|---|
| EXP04, GL395 |

**(d)**

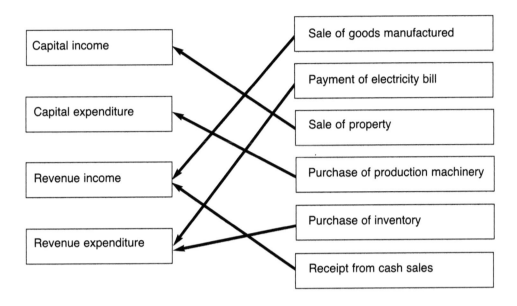